*Uncle Arthur's*

# BEDTIME
# STORIES

## VOLUME FOUR

T. K. MARTIN

**Uncle Arthur Is Never so Happy as When He Is in the Company of Children.
Here They Are in Beautiful Golden Gate Park, San Francisco, California**

# *Uncle Arthur's*
# BEDTIME STORIES

## VOLUME FOUR

### By ARTHUR S. MAXWELL

REVIEW AND HERALD, WASHINGTON, D.C.

# CONTENTS

## VOLUME IV

# Lesson Index

8

## The Pictures

*In This Volume Were Drawn by Harry Anderson, Harvey Fuller, Arlo Greer, Russell Harlan, Gedge Harmon, Iris Johnson, Manning de V. Lee, Don Nelson, Vernon Nye, and Herbert Rudeen.*

# Preface

*P*ERHAPS YOU NEVER thought about it before, but when you began to read this book you joined the ranks of millions of boys and girls and fathers and mothers who have read, and are still reading, *Bedtime Stories*. Exactly how many nephews and nieces I have, nobody knows. I gave up counting them when the number passed ten million. And that was years ago.

It is really a very thrilling thought that all over the world there are happy little families where night after night the children go to sleep on *Bedtime Stories*. Hundreds of thousands of them are in the United States. Tens of thousands more are in Canada, England, Australia, New Zealand, South Africa—indeed, in every part of the English-speaking world. In addition, there are many others in Japan, China, the Malay States, Germany, Norway, Sweden, Denmark, and other lands where these books have been translated into the native languages. Just suppose all these children, from all these scattered places, could meet for just one hour! What a wonderful gathering it would be! What a grand time we would have together! Alas, there isn't a hall anywhere big enough to hold them all. Even the Yankee Stadium wouldn't have anywhere near enough room for everybody. Maybe we'll have to forgo the meeting till we all get into God's gloryland.

Meanwhile, you could write me; couldn't you? Surely. You will find my address at the bottom of the next page. Tell me which story you like best. And if you have had some very interesting experience that has taught you a beautiful lesson, tell me about that too. It might make another story for my big family of nephews and nieces to enjoy.

That reminds me. People keep on asking, Where do you get all those lovely stories? I'll tell you. Out of the hearts of little children. Of course, some come from their mothers, some from their fathers, and some from their aunts and uncles, but most of them come from the boys and girls themselves, who tell me of the wonderful things that have happened in their own lives. That is why I can always say that *Bedtime Stories* are true. For the most part they have happened to children whom I have met, or who have written me in their own handwriting. Now and then, just for a change, I tell a story from history, about something that happened in the long ago, but these are the exceptions; and even these stories, like all the rest, have one basic purpose— to teach some lovely lesson that will build character and lead boys and girls in the paths of truth and right.

That this fourth volume, with all its beautiful pictures and glowing colors, may be a constant source of joy and blessing to children everywhere is my earnest hope and prayer.

UNCLE ARTHUR.

"Twin Oaks"
101 North El Monte Avenue,
Los Altos, California.

Johann Was Homeless, Tired, Hungry, and Discouraged as He Trudged Out Into
the Night and Stood Before a Little Old Cottage With a Light in It

# The House That Glowed

*J*T WAS CHRISTMAS Eve, and poor little Johann, driven out of his home by an angry and brutal stepfather, was trudging wearily through the snow.

His coat was ragged and sodden with melted snow. His shoes were worn and split at the seams, so that his feet were numb with cold. His quaint cap, pulled well down over his ears and forehead, had a gaping tear that let in the biting wind.

Night was falling, and the gathering darkness found the homeless little boy still plodding on his sad and lonely way.

"If only I could find some shelter, some place where I could get warm, and the wind would not chill me so," he thought to himself. "If only someone would give me some food to eat and something hot to drink!"

Coming to the edge of the forest, he caught sight of a little village nestling in the valley below, with several fine, large houses dotting the hillside all around. Lights were already twinkling in the windows, while the

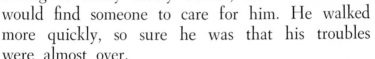

smoke from many chimneys, curling upward, blended with the murky sky.

A great new hope sprang up in little Johann's heart. Here at last, among so many lovely homes, he would find someone to care for him. He walked more quickly, so sure he was that his troubles were almost over.

Soon he came to the entrance of a fine, big mansion. There were many lights in the windows and a very bright one over the front door. "Surely," he thought, "people who could live in such a house must have lots of money and would be only too pleased to help a poor, hungry little boy."

Very bravely he walked up to the front door, and by standing on tiptoe, managed to reach the bell. He pushed it hard, and there was such a noise inside that it frightened him. But he was more frightened still when the great oak door was thrown back and a big man dressed in the finest clothes looked out at him.

"Did you ring that bell?" asked the haughty butler, frowning.

"Y-y-y-yes," stammered Johann, "I-I-I'm very cold and hungry, and I thought you——"

"This is Christmas Eve," snapped the butler, "and the house is full of guests. I'm sorry, but we haven't

time to bother with the likes of you just now. Good night."

And the door was shut.

"Oh!" said Johann to himself, "I never thought anyone would do that. But perhaps they are too busy here. I must try somewhere else.

So he walked on down into the village itself, passing by the other big mansions for fear the people inside might also be too busy to care about hungry little boys on Christmas Eve.

From the first house he reached there came sounds of music and laughter, and feeling sure that there must be very friendly people living there, he knocked gently on the door. But there was so much noise inside that he had to knock again and again, each time louder than before.

At last the door swung open, and a young man wearing a funny paper cap looked out.

"Excuse me," said Johann, "but I wondered if you could——"

"Sorry," cried the gay young man, "we're having a Christmas Eve party in here, and we can't stop now."

"But please, please!" pleaded Johann.

"Sorry; good night!" cried the young man. And bang! the door was shut.

Terribly disappointed, Johann went next door, but

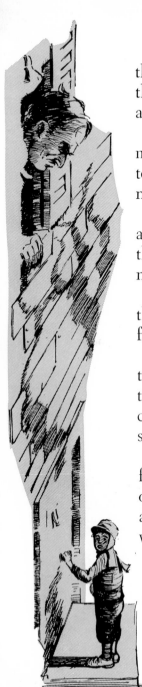

the people there were making so much noise
that they didn't even hear him at all, loud
as he knocked.

At the next house a crabby old gentleman looked out of an upstairs window and
told him to run home and not bother the
neighbors. Run home, indeed!

At another house he was told to call
again another day. They would help him
then perhaps, the people said. But he
needed help now!

So, going from house to house through
the entire village, he sought shelter and
food, and found none.

Almost hopeless and heartbroken, he
trudged out into the night, leaving the
twinkling lights behind him. He felt he
could lie down and die in the road, he was
so tired, so hungry, so discouraged.

Just then he happened to look up and
found himself passing a tiny, tumble-down
old cottage, so dark and dismal that he probably wouldn't have seen it at all but for the
white carpet of snow on the ground showing it up. A blind covered the one
little window, but faint streaks of light
gleamed through cracks in the woodwork.

Johann stood still and wondered what he should do. Should he knock here?

What would be the use? Surely if the people who lived in all the big houses—who had money for lovely parties and things—couldn't afford to help a poor boy, how could the folk in a house like this? No, it was of no use. Better not bother them. Better go on and die in the woods.

Then he thought again. He had knocked at so many houses, there could be no harm in trying one more. So he turned from the road up the snow-covered garden path and tapped gently on the door.

A moment later the door opened cautiously, and an elderly woman peered out. "Bless my soul!" she exclaimed. "Whatever are you doing out there in the cold tonight?"

"Please——" began Johann.

But before he could say another word she had flung the door wide open and dragged him inside.

"You poor little child," she exclaimed. "Deary, deary me! You look so cold and hungry. Half starved, or I'm mistaken. And wet through. Let's get those things off at once. Wait a moment while I stir up the fire and put the kettle on."

Johann looked about him and saw that the little one-roomed cottage was as bare as could be, without even a carpet on the floor. The light he had seen through the cracks came from one lone candle set on the mantlepiece. But he hadn't time to see much else, for the kind woman was soon stripping off his wet rags, wrapping him in a blanket, and setting him up at the table before a bowl of steaming soup.

Then she went back to stir the pot on the stove. As she did so she suddenly noticed that something strange was happening. She looked up.

Was it a dream, or were her eyes deceiving her? The candlelight had given place to a warm and lovely glow that seemed to be getting brighter every minute, filling every corner of the cottage with a heavenly radiance. Every drab piece of furniture seemed to be shining and glistening like burnished gold, as when God filled the temple with His glory.

And the rich man, looking down from his mansion on the hill, suddenly exclaimed, "There's a strange light in the valley. Look! Widow Greatheart's cottage is on fire!"

The news spread swiftly from house to house, and soon all the gay parties were abandoned as the people, wrapping themselves up in their coats and shawls, rushed out to see what was the matter.

They saw the light, too, and running toward the widow's cottage, beheld the poor tumble-down old building glowing like an alabaster bowl. Very excited, they gathered around it.

Peering inside, all they could see was the dear old woman caring for the very same little boy who had called that night at all their homes.

Then, as the light faded, they knocked on the door to ask anxiously what could have happened.

"I really do not know," said Widow Greatheart, with a smile of wondrous joy and satisfaction on her face. "I just seemed to hear a voice saying to me, 'Inasmuch as ye have done it unto one of the least of these My children, ye have done it unto Me.'"

# Little Missionary

*T*HERE ARE TWO things that you should know about Betty. First, when this wonderful event happened, she was just about eight years old. Second, she had a smile "like the smile of an angel." And that must be a very lovely smile, I should say.

Oh, yes, there was something else about her that you should know. She loved to do "missionary work," as she called it. Every chance she had she would go out on the streets of the city in which she lived and give away tracts and papers and little bound portions of Scripture which told of the love of Jesus. So sweetly did she smile up at the people that they couldn't help taking a tract from her. She was so very, very pleasant and friendly that they just had to take one.

Then one Sunday afternoon as Betty was walking along, smiling away at everybody as she handed out her "missionary papers," she suddenly looked ahead

22

and saw something that for a moment made her very much frightened.

A man was coming toward her, staggering along the sidewalk.

He was drunk.

Now, most little girls—and some little boys—would run away from a drunk man. But not Betty. She was a brave little girl. She was doing "missionary work for Jesus," and she would not be turned back.

So very boldly she went up to the drunk man, and smiling her lovely angel smile, held up a little pocket Gospel.

He stopped and looked at her.

"May I give you this little book?" she asked.

"W-w-what little book?" he said gruffly.

"This little book," said Betty, holding the little

Gospel higher still. "And please, sir, it will do you lots of good."

The drunk man, arrested by the saintly little face and the lovely smile, took the book in his hand.

"H-h-how much is it?" he hiccoughed.

"Oh, nothing at

all, please, sir," said Betty. "We don't charge for it. We give it to you to read. And really, it *will* do you lots of good."

The poor man slipped the book into his pocket.

Betty passed on, and for a moment the man stood there speechless. Then he, too, went on his way. But he could not get the little girl out of his mind. That angel smile fascinated him.

After a while he took the little book out of his coat pocket and began to read. It was a tiny copy of the Gospel of John.

He read on and on, and as he read of the love of God for the poor and the outcast, his heart was touched.

"God so loved the world," he read, "that He gave His only begotten Son, that whosoever believeth in Him should not perish, but have everlasting life."

Farther on he found this beautiful promise: "Whatsoever ye shall ask in My name, that will I do, that the Father may be glorified in the Son. If ye shall ask any thing in My name, I will do it." John 14:13, 14.

Then he read: "If ye love Me, keep My commandments. And I will pray the Father, and He shall give you another Comforter, that He may abide with you for ever." Verses 15, 16.

At last he turned his eyes to heaven and prayed

that God would forgive him for all his sins and help him to live a better life.

He was converted. He went to church, and was baptized.

Exactly one year after he met Betty, I met him. He was then the deacon of a large church in California. He told me that before Betty smiled at him and gave him that little book, he had no work, no home, no money—nothing at all.

Now he is happy and prosperous, and all his needs are supplied.

What a beautiful thing it was that Betty did! And what a wonderful star she will have in her crown one day for bringing this soul to Jesus!

God bless all little girls, and all little boys, too, who go out to do "missionary work" like this.

# Finding's Keeping

*J*ESSIE WAS SO EXCITED when she came in to dinner that she could hardly speak.

"Mamma, look what I've found!" she panted.

"Whatever do you have there?" exclaimed Mamma. "Why, it looks like a purse."

"Yes, it is," cried Jessie. "It's just the dearest little purse, and there's a lot of money in it, too. Just think what I'll be able to buy with it."

"Let me see it," said Mamma, taking the purse and looking inside. "You're right, Jessie, there is quite a lot of money in it—nearly four dollars."

"Oh!" cried Jessie, mouth wide open and eyes sparkling.

"But you wouldn't want to keep this yourself, would you?" asked Mamma.

"Why not?" asked Jessie, a trace of fear in her voice. "Finding's keeping, isn't it?"

"Sometimes in a game, perhaps," said Mamma, "but not with somebody else's purse. Why, just think! Perhaps some poor woman dropped it on her way to do some shopping, and this money may be all she had to provide for her family the rest of the week."

"But, Mamma, I found it."

"I know you did, dear, but she lost it, and it's really still hers, at least until you've tried every way you know how to find her. You want to think how you would feel if you lost your purse and somebody found it, and kept it. You wouldn't like that, would you?"

"I hadn't thought of that," said Jessie. "I don't suppose I would like it."

"I don't think you would either," said Mamma, "and if we are going to do unto others as we want them to do unto us——"

"I suppose I'd better take it back," interrupted Jessie. "But what shall I do with it?"

"The proper thing is to take it to the police station," said Mamma, "and they will keep it there and see if anybody comes for it. If not, then they will give it back to you."

"All right, then," said Jessie, smiling. "I'll take it right away. That poor woman may be worrying dreadfully about it."

So off she ran as fast as she could go.

On the way she met a school friend.

"What's the hurry?" asked Marjorie.

"Oh, I found a purse in the street, and I'm just taking it to the police station."

"Any money in it?"

"Four dollars."

"Then you're going the wrong way," said Marjorie. "Why don't you keep it?"

"Oh, I couldn't," said Jessie. "Some poor woman may be in a dreadful state about it, and I want to get it back to her as soon as I can."

"You are stupid," said Marjorie. "Why should you worry about that, I'd like to know?"

"Maybe I am stupid," said Jessie, a little worried, "but I'm going to take it anyway."

Arrived at the police station, Jessie explained her mission. The policeman beamed on her, and said he thought she was the most honest girl in town. Then he made a note of her name and address and the nature and contents of the bag, and Jessie departed feeling as happy as if someone had left her a legacy of a million dollars.

And that was not the end of her joy.

That night there was a knock at the front door, and Jessie, opening it, recognized the minister's wife, one of her best friends.

"Jessie," said the visitor, "I've just found my bag at the police station, and they told me there that it was you who took it in. I want to thank you ever so much, and maybe you would let me give you something to show you how very grateful I am."

"Oh, no, no, no!" exclaimed Jessie. "I wouldn't dream of it. Please don't. I'm so happy to have helped you and that you have it back again. I had no idea that it could possibly have belonged to you, or I would have brought it straight to your home."

"I know you would," said the minister's wife. "And I do want you to know, Jessie, how very much I appreciate what you did. I shall not forget it."

When her visitor had gone, Jessie looked at

Mamma, and a strange, understanding smile came over both their faces.

"What a fortunate thing it was that I took it back," said Jessie. "Just suppose I had gone to church with that bag in my hand! It makes me go hot and cold all over just to think of it. And if I had spent her money, I never could have forgiven myself."

"Well," said Mamma, shaking her head, "it's just one more proof that it always pays to do right."

# Why the World Felt Sad

*A*LL THE WORLD FELT
sad when King Edward VIII gave up his throne.

For days before it happened, people scarcely talked
of anything else. The story filled the newspapers in
every land on earth.

In busy cities, faraway villages, dreary deserts, it
was the one topic of conversation.

At an isolated garage in the lonely wilderness of
Arizona the first question I was asked was not, "How
much gasoline do you want?" but, "What of the king?"

Everywhere it was the same. In churches, in
schools, in hotels, in restaurants, in shops, always I
met the same anxious inquiry, "What of the king?"

And when he spoke the final word of abdication,
a hush seemed to fall upon mankind. In some places
business ceased for the day.

Why did men love him so? More than anything
else, I think, it was due to his thoughtfulness for others,
coupled with a keen insight into their needs. There
was something about his unaffected friendliness toward

31

everybody, and particularly his genuine interest in the common people, that won the affection of all—Englishmen, Australians, Canadians, South Africans, Americans, and people of all tongues and climes.

Do you remember that lovely thing he did just before the *Queen Mary* was launched on the Clyde?

It is said that he walked seven miles that day, up and down that wonderful vessel, inspecting every part of her from the engine room to the bridge. Then when he had finished, and everybody thought he would be tired and ready to go back home, to the amazement and concern of his private detectives, he plunged through the crowd into the homes of the people around the docks. Most of them live in slums, the sort of places

32

kings don't usually visit, but that made no difference to King Edward.

In and out of the houses he went, talking with the astonished mothers and children as if they belonged to Sandringham. "If it is right to visit the *Queen Mary*, it is surely right to visit the people who made her." That was his attitude, and when the story appeared in the papers the next day, you could almost feel the thrill of delight that swept over the country.

Which reminds me of another kindly act, of exceptional graciousness, performed by him some years before, when he was Prince of Wales.

He had been asked to visit a private hospital for crippled soldiers. Arriving there on the appointed day,

he went from one to the other of the poor, suffering men, speaking some cheering word to each of them and encouraging all by his presence. On reaching the door, he was about to leave, when he inquired whether he had seen all the patients.

"No," was the reply, "there are seven others, but they are so seriously disfigured that we felt you might not wish to see them."

"I must see them," said the prince.

At this he was ushered into the sanctuary of exceptional suffering. Going quietly from bed to bed, he spoke in kind, gentle tones to each man, thanking him for all he had done for England.

Again he was leaving, when he said to his guide, "You said there were seven men, and I have seen only six. Where is the other?"

"Your Highness," was the reply, "nobody can see this man, he is so terribly maimed—disfigured out of the likeness of humanity."

"I must see him also," said the prince.

"Better not, sir; it is terrible."

"Still, I wish to see him."

They went in together, the prince, very pale, walking firmly to the bedside. With bowed head he looked down upon this poor wreck of humanity that could neither see nor hear him.

Then, very slowly, he stooped and kissed the man's face. It was the highest homage he could pay, and surely the most gracious act a king of England ever did.

This beautiful story, so often told and retold already, will go echoing on through all the years to come. It has eternal qualities, telling of a royal love for a suffering subject, like the love of God for us all.

No wonder the whole world loved King Edward VIII, and sorrowed as he left his throne.

As king he may be forgotten, but as a friend of the people he will be loved forever.

Love begets love, and it is deeds like these—humble, thoughtful, gentle, generous—that win the hearts of men.

# The Wrong Key

*H*ENRY WAS GETTING angrier and angrier. On the table in front of him was a small black box given him by his Father, in which he used to keep his most precious things, so that his little brothers would not tamper with them.

It was locked, and Henry was trying to unlock it. But it just wouldn't unlock.

He tried and tried and tried, but all in vain.

He pushed the key in and pulled it out—and pushed it in again, turning it this way and that. Still nothing happened.

He banged and shook the box and turned it upside down and back again, but without result.

And he was in such a hurry. He had promised to meet a friend downtown half an hour ago; but the stamps he was to take with him were in the box. Still in the box! Why wouldn't it open?

Mother came in, sympathetic as usual.

"What's the matter?" she asked.

"This box!" snapped Henry. "It just won't open."

"Let me try," said Mother.

36

"No use," said Henry. "I've tried over and over again."

"Maybe you have the wrong key," suggested Mother gently.

"No, I haven't," growled Henry angrily; "surely I should know the key to my own box."

"You should," said Mother, "but everybody makes mistakes sometimes."

"Well, I haven't," growled Henry. "Yet it won't open. Oh, dear!"

Mother withdrew.

Henry went on turning the key.

At last, in fierce impatience, he seized a pair of pliers and gave it an added twist.

Of course, it broke in the lock.

"There! Now I can't open it at all," he cried, tears coming into his eyes.

Suddenly he caught sight of his hammer.

"I *will* get it open," he said, "whatever happens."

A moment later the house echoed to the sound of heavy blows.

Bang, bang, bang!

"Got it," he whispered, as the lock burst and the lid sprang open.

"What have you done?" cried Mother, as she ran into the room.

"Done?" said Henry. "Opened the box, of course."

"You have," said Mother, "and you'll never shut it again. See, it is broken beyond repair. And that box cost six dollars."

"Did it?" exclaimed Henry, amazed.

"Indeed it did," said Mother, "and it will cost you all that to get another one."

"Phew!" said Henry, beginning to regret his impatience.

"By the way," said Mother, picking up a small, shining object from the floor, "what's this?"

"That? That's the right key to the box," said Henry in dismay. "I must have had the wrong one in the lock all the time. Why *didn't* I see it? And now my box is all smashed!"

"You know," said Mother quietly, "it never does pay to lose one's patience. We always make mistakes when we do."

Henry said nothing, but as he hurried down the street to meet his friend, he thought seriously.

It will be a long time, I should say, before he does such a foolish thing again.

# Helping Daddy

*D*ADDY WAS DOWN IN the garden, putting some seeds in the ground. They were pea seeds, and Daddy was making a straight row so that when the peas came up they would look nice.

Mabel was watching Daddy, and she thought that she would like to sow some pea seeds too.

So she got her little spade and dug a hole in the ground. Then she came to Daddy and said, "Please, Daddy, give me some of your pea seeds for me to sow."

So Daddy gave her some of his pea seeds, and Mabel dropped them into the big hole she had made and covered them over with earth. Daddy looked round to see what she was doing, and he said, "Why, my little girl, those seeds are too far down. They will never be able to find their way up."

"Well," said Mabel, "I 'specks they will grow all right, but I think I will sow some more in case they don't."

But Daddy had already used all the pea seeds, and Mabel was very much disappointed. And do you know what she did? You could never guess.

Well, when Daddy wasn't looking, she went over to where he had planted his row of peas, and poking her hands down into the earth, brought up some of the seeds. Just then Daddy looked round and said, "Oh, you naughty little girl! What are you doing?"

"Just getting some more seeds," said Mabel, " 'cos I didn't have enough."

"Well, I never!" said Daddy. "Digging up my nice new row of seeds. That is naughty of you, Mabel."

"But they will grow just as well here as there," said Mabel, digging another deep hole and dropping in the seeds she had taken from Daddy's row.

"No, they won't," said Daddy. "You mustn't take seeds that do not belong to you. If you had left them

where they were, we should have had some lovely peas from them someday. But now they will never grow."

Later in the spring, Daddy and Mabel were down in the garden again.

"What a lovely row of peas!" said Mabel.

"Yes," said Daddy, "it's just spoiled by a little gap up at the other end, isn't it?"

"Yes," said Mabel, "is that where I took some out?"

"Yes," said Daddy, "and where are they now?"

"I can't see them anywhere," said Mabel.

"No," said Daddy, "and you never will. Nobody ever gains by doing naughty things. I think they must have gone down the other way."

And they had.

42

# The Letter to Mamma

*M*AMMA WAS VERY ILL, and some people had come in a strange car with a red cross on it and carried her away to the hospital.

Poor little Ted and Tod were very sad and lonely. They had never felt so lonely before. How they did long for Mamma to come back again! Every time a car went by, they would run to the window to see whether the car with the red cross on it had come back again. Poor little Tod cried himself to sleep every night.

"Mamma said we were to write to her often," said Ted one day. "Shall we do it now?"

Tod said, "Yes," and they set to work. Tod found some paper and a bottle of ink. When he opened the ink bottle, the stopper ran around all over the paper and made a big black mark. So they decided to write the letter in pencil.

"Mamma won't mind the blots, I expect," said Ted. "Now, what shall we say?"

"Tell her I want her to come back soon," said Tod.

"I will," said Ted.

So they wrote, and here is the letter:

Dear Darling mother,

Please come back soon,
we hope you are getting
better. We love you so
much. We want you home
home again. Tod has lost
a button off his coat.
You must not get sick
again. Pussy has got some
kittens. We say our pra-
yers every night. We

ask Jesus to make you
better Tod say come back
soon, and so do I.
With Lots of Love and
kisses from your lovely boys

Tod and Ted,

And then they sealed the envelope, got a stamp from auntie, and went out to put the letter in the mail-box.

Tod said he wanted to mail the letter, but when they got to the box they found he could not quite reach the place where the letters go in. So Ted lifted Tod as high as he could, and Tod poked the letter into the box.

And when Mamma opened the letter the next morning she was so pleased she said she felt better already.

# Why Mary Cheered Up

*T*HERE," SAID MARY, flinging her school satchel down on the kitchen table, "I'm never going to try again."

"Why, Mary dear, what has happened?" asked Mother. "You were so happy when you went off to school this morning."

"Maybe I was," replied Mary sadly, "but I'm not now."

"But why, dear?"

"Teacher put up the examination results today, and I'm twelfth again. I did so want to be at the top this time."

Mary buried her face in her hands and began to cry.

"Cheer up," said Mother, coming over to Mary's side and putting one arm around her. "It might have been much worse, you know. Why, you might have been at the bottom, and that would have been terrible, wouldn't it?"

"I suppose it would," said Mary, "but I'm never anything else but twelfth. I simply can't get to the top.

I've never had a prize, and I suppose I never shall. I am just a dull, stupid dunce, that's what I am, and I shall never be any good at all."

"Why, Mary dear, you'll be lots of good someday. And there are some subjects in which you have had nearly perfect marks. Didn't you get ninety-five per cent in botany the other day? That should cheer you up."

"It doesn't. Nothing cheers me up," wailed Mary.

"Let me tell you a story, then," said Mother. "You've heard of Mr. Baldwin, once prime minister of England?"

"I'm not sure," said Mary.

"Well, do you know, when he was a boy and took the entrance examination at the famous school known as Harrow, he failed?"

"Did he?" said Mary.

"He surely did," said Mother. "And another boy who failed in that same examination was called Freddie Smith. When he grew up he became Lord Birkenhead, one of the greatest lawyers of his time."

"Perhaps there's hope for me yet," said Mary, brightening up a little.

"Let me tell you some more," continued Mother. "You've heard of Clive of India. Teacher may have mentioned him at school sometime."

"Yes."

"Well, it is said of him that he was the despair of his teachers. As for Nelson, the great admiral, when he went to school, he was a very poor scholar. I don't suppose his teacher ever thought he would win Trafalgar or the battle of the Nile."

"I don't suppose he did," said Mary.

"Then there is Sir Ernest Shackleton," went on Mother, "that noble explorer who went to the South Pole. You would hardly believe it, Mary, but as a boy he never rose high in his school, and couldn't apply himself to his books at all."

"Fancy all those great men being like me," said Mary, a smile beginning to curl around the corners of her mouth, and a merry twinkle showing in her eye.

"There are many more people like you, dear. Abraham Lincoln himself had a big struggle when he was

young. Nobody in those days dreamed that he would ever be President of the United States."

"Well!" exclaimed Mary. "I thought all these great people were always at the top in school."

"It's a strange thing," said Mother, "but few of them were. Many of the most useful men who have ever lived simply couldn't get on well at school. Being at the top in school doesn't mean that you are going to be at the top in everything all your life."

"But the top girls and boys seem so bright," said Mary; "they always get good marks and can answer so much more quickly than I can."

"Yes," said Mother, "but remember the tortoise and the hare. It isn't always the fastest that gets there first."

"I'm sure I'm as slow as a tortoise, anyway," said Mary.

"Then cheer up and keep on pegging away," said Mother. "You're bound to win someday if you do."

"Oh, well," said Mary, springing to her feet with new hope in her heart. "I suppose I'll have to try a bit harder next time." And she did.

Eric, Blushing, Came Forward to Receive His Award. "Please," He Stammered, "Would—Would You Mind if I Had the Second Prize Instead?"

# Four Chocolate Eggs

*W*HAT EXCITEMENT
there was in the classroom that morning! What eagerness and attention!

You see, teacher had just announced that she was
going to make a little gift to the boy or girl who answered the most questions correctly in the tests they
were going to have that day.

What it was, she wouldn't say, except that it was
very nice, very pretty, and very tasty.

Of course, that last word set everybody's mouth
watering.

"Something tasty!" said Ted Jones. "I could use
that right now."

"And so could I," said Eric Foster, whose Mother
had been so busy that morning looking after his two
little brothers and his baby sister that she had forgotten
to put up his lunch.

"But I would rather have something pretty," said
Peggy Phillips, just like a girl.

"I wonder where she put it," said Peter Rich. "Perhaps we could take a peep at it when she's not looking."

Teacher heard that.

"Oh, no, you can't," she said. "It is put away safely in my desk, and no one will see it until the tests are all over."

Peter blushed and wished he hadn't spoken.

Then the tests began, and how everyone did work! When teacher asked the questions aloud, hands flashed up all over the room and waved about like trees in a high wind. When the answers had to be written, there was an unusual silence, broken only by the frantic scratching of pens on paper.

It was lots of fun, and everyone had high hopes of winning the prize.

Slowly the hours dragged by, with Ted and Peter and Peggy and all the rest becoming more and more certain that they were going to win, and poor Eric getting hungrier and hungrier every minute and imagining what he would do with the prize if he should win.

At last the tests were all over, the answers all checked, and the marks all totaled up.

Who had won?

"Now," said teacher, "I am almost ready to tell you who has won the prize."

The silence was so deep that you could have heard a pin drop.

"It's going to be me," whispered Peter to Peggy.

Teacher heard again. What good ears some teachers do have!

"I'm afraid you are wrong, Peter," she said. "The prize goes to——"

"Peggy," "Ted," "Tommy," "Dick," "Amy," "Dora," came a chorus from all over the room.

"No," said teacher, smiling, "you're all wrong. Little Eric is the winner, beating Peggy by just one mark." Peggy groaned.

At this moment teacher opened her desk and produced a big chocolate egg, tied with a piece of wide blue ribbon.

"How lovely!" cried everybody. "Lucky boy," said Ted.

"Now just a moment," said teacher. "I have a second prize. It is in this box."

Everyone looked and saw four little chocolate eggs. They were good, too, but not so attractive as the big one in the blue ribbon.

Eric, blushing, came forward to receive his prize. He had looked at both prizes and was thinking hard.

Teacher smiled at him and told him how pleased she was that he had done so well. Then she proceeded to hand him the big chocolate egg. But Eric's hands were behind his back, his face scarlet.

"Please," he stammered, "would—would you mind if I had the second prize instead?"

Everybody gasped, and teacher was so surprised that she hardly knew what to say. She had thought there wasn't a child in the room who would not have been thrilled to take the beautiful gift she was offering. "But," she thought, "Eric is always a good boy, and he must have a reason for his unusual request." So she gave him the second prize, and Peggy was surely delighted to get the first prize after all.

Of course, every boy and girl in the class wanted to know why Eric had done such a strange thing, but he wouldn't say a word. He just ran off home with his precious little box under his arm, not even opening it to take one little bite.

But if any of Eric's school friends could have peeped inside his home that evening, they would have found out all about it. For there, sitting on the kitchen floor, were four of the happiest little children you could imagine. Just three boys and one baby girl.

And they were all, in an ecstasy of delight, munching chocolate eggs.

# A Tale of Two Sparrows

*M*R. AND MRS. SPARROW were just married, and they were looking for a nice place where they could build their nest.

They flew about for a long time without any success. Mrs. Sparrow was rather hard to please. Whenever Mr. Sparrow found a nice little corner that he thought would do, and came swooping down through the air to tell her so, Mrs. Sparrow would say, "Oh, that's not at all suitable for me, Mr. Sparrow. I must have something much better than that for my home."

At last Mr. Sparrow got so discouraged that he said he wouldn't look any more, and that Mrs. Sparrow, if she were so particular, had better look for herself.

Mrs. Sparrow took him at his word and said that if she couldn't find a nice place in half the time that Mr. Sparrow had taken, she would know the reason why.

So off flew Mrs. Sparrow to see what she could do. In a little while she returned.

"I've found a wonderful place," she said. "It's warm and cozy, well protected from the weather, and the way in is so small that no one else will ever be able to find it; so we shall be quite by ourselves, with no neighbors to annoy us. You'll be able to sleep late in the morning, for there will be no other birds around to start singing too early."

"My dear!" cried Mr. Sparrow, "where can it be? Do show me at once. I'm so glad you have been so successful."

"Ah," said Mrs. Sparrow, "it takes me to find a home. I'll show you. You come along with me."

With that Mrs. Sparrow hopped off her perch and flew high in the air, with Mr. Sparrow following meekly at a respectful distance behind.

On and on they flew.

"Where are you taking me?" asked Mr. Sparrow, getting alarmed.

"You'll find out in a minute," said Mrs. Sparrow.

They were approaching a lofty church tower, and Mrs. Sparrow seemed to be flying to the very top of it.

"My dear, do be careful," called Mr. Sparrow. "This is very dangerous."

Mrs. Sparrow flew on as if she had not heard him. At last she alighted where a small window had been broken at the top of the tower. In a moment she had popped inside.

Poor Mr. Sparrow followed, very much alarmed and wondering what terrible thing would happen to them.

"Look," said Mrs. Sparrow. "Isn't this ideal? The very thing we have been looking for! Dry, fairly clean, and very private. I told you, Mr. Sparrow, that I would find the right place."

"But, my dear," said poor Mr. Sparrow, greatly agitated, "do you think it's all right? Is it safe?"

"Safe!" cried Mrs. Sparrow. "Of course it's safe. Now please get busy and bring all the straw you can find. We might as well make ourselves comfortable as soon as we can."

Very meekly Mr. Sparrow obeyed. In a little while he was back again, bringing a few pieces of straw in his beak. By this time Mrs. Sparrow had selected an attractive spot for the nest in between a number of wooden pipes. Mr. Sparrow put down his pieces of straw and went out in search of more.

It did not take them very long to build their nest, and in a day or two they were settled down, ready to enjoy a well-earned rest.

All at once something terrible happened. It was on a Wednesday evening about seven o'clock. Mr. and Mrs. Sparrow were settled comfortably in bed when suddenly they were awakened by a terrific noise. Groans and roars came from the big pipes, whines and shrieks from the little pipes. The whole place rocked and shook.

"My dear! My dear!" cried Mr. Sparrow. "What's the matter? What can have happened? Are you safe?"

But Mrs. Sparrow was not there to hear. Already she was at the broken window, shrieking at Mr. Sparrow to escape for his life. And without another thought they both jumped from the top of the tower out into the dark, cold night.

Probably those poor little sparrows will never know

what really happened that terrible evening. As long as they live they will tell their friends how they lost their beautiful home, recounting in awed whispers the terrors they suffered in the haunted tower.

The fact was, of course, that they had merely tried to make their nest in the church organ loft. And the awful sounds they had heard that Wednesday evening were really the hymns the organist was playing for the prayer meeting.

To the people in the church the music was beautiful. "How lovely!" they all had said. "What delightful harmonies! What a wonderful organist!"

But to the poor little sparrows in the loft it had seemed like an earthquake and a hurricane combined.

All of which goes to tell us that things are not always what they seem. And sometimes children, like

the sparrows, are frightened merely because they do not understand. And sometimes, too, they grumble and growl because they are not yet old enough to appreciate the meaning of things beyond them.

Perhaps you have heard a little boy say sometime, "I don't like going to church. I never can understand a word the preacher says, and some of the hymns have no tune to them at all." Someday, however, he will understand the preacher and rejoice in his inspiring words. And someday the hymns that have seemed to have the least tune in them will be loved and prized most of all.

Perhaps, too, you have heard a little girl say, "I don't know why I have to put up with so much. I don't have the nice things other children have."

That *is* hard to understand, I admit. But when you feel like that, just think that Someone is playing on the organ of your life. To you the notes sound harsh and discordant, but the Organist knows what He is playing, and someday you will understand how lovely was the tune that He composed.

So when things go wrong and you are tempted to judge quickly and unkindly, just wait a little while and think of the sparrows in the tower.

MANNING DE V. LEE, ARTIST

**What a Wonderful Time They Had! Barbara Sang While Richard Played His Violin, and Bessie Knocked at the Doors and Smiled Sweetly**

# Barbara's Talent

*M*OTHER!" GASPED Barbara, rushing into the dining room and flopping down in an armchair, "I've got to earn some money."

"My dear!" exclaimed Mother. "Whatever is the matter with the child now!"

"Yes, I must," went on Barbara. "It's most important, and I have got to earn a lot very quickly."

Mother began to look serious.

"What for?" she asked.

"Well," said Barbara very excitedly, "Mr. Walters, the new superintendent, told us in Sabbath school this morning that if we didn't give $250 for missions within the next two weeks, Mr. James would have to come back from India right away."

"Why, we've only just sent him out," said Mother.

"I know; that's just the trouble," said Barbara. "Mr. Walters said that everybody thought there would be enough money to keep him there. But there isn't. Something's gone wrong, he said, and the Mission Board is

very hard up. So there, if we don't raise the $250 in two weeks, well, Mr. James comes home."

"That sounds very serious," said Mother. "But Barbara dear, *we* can't raise $250 in just two weeks."

"Oh, no," said Barbara, "not we by ourselves. Each class has agreed to raise $25. Each one in the class has promised to raise $2.50."

"Have you promised $2.50, Barbara?" gasped Mother.

"Why, of course," said Barbara. "I couldn't do anything else, could I? And that's why I've got to earn some money. How can I do it, Mother dear?"

"Well," said Mother, "it's all very well for you to promise money like that, but I haven't got it to give you, dear, even if you help me ever so much. You know Daddy has not been earning much lately."

"I know," said Barbara, on the verge of tears, "but I—surely—can—earn it—somehow. Er—er I must keep my—er—promise, now I've made it."

Barbara began to cry.

"Never mind, dear," said Mother, "we'll find some

64

way out, surely. But you have taken on a difficult task, and no mistake."

"I did so want to help," said Barbara.

"I'm sure you did," said Mother, putting her arms around Barbara's neck. "Let's think it over a while and see what can be done."

That evening, as the family gathered around the fire for prayers, Mother read to them the parable of the talents. As the story proceeded, Barbara's face grew more and more serious. She could see the man with the five talents trading with them and earning five talents more to give to the King. Then she saw the man with the two talents earning two talents. And then at last she saw the man with one talent burying it in the earth and having nothing—nothing—nothing!—to give to the Lord at His return.

She became very serious.

"What's troubling you, dear?" asked Mother as she closed the Book.

"Oh, I feel just like the man with one talent who didn't earn anything at all. Only there's just this difference, that I don't have even *one* talent."

"Well, Barbara, I didn't think you would take it so much to heart. And you have talents, many of them."

"No, I haven't. I haven't any at all. I'm just no good, and I'll never be able to earn that money."

"O Barbara, don't be so sad. You certainly have one talent anyway, and perhaps God will help you to use that to His glory."

"I'm sure I haven't," said Barbara.

"You have forgotten your voice," answered Mother. "You know how beautifully you can sing when you want to. Perhaps—who knows?—you may be able to keep your promise by singing for Jesus."

"Me?" asked Barbara. "How could I? No one would listen to a little girl like me."

"I'm not so sure," said Mother. "You seem to have forgotten that it is nearly Christmas time, and people will listen to children then, you know, that is, if they sing nicely and reverently."

"Do you mean that I could go out and sing carols at people's houses?"

"Well, not by yourself. But I've got an idea. There's Richard with his violin, and Bessie—she can sing too.

I believe that the three of you might do wonderfully well. At any rate we could think about it."

A new light entered Barbara's eyes. Hope stirred anew within her little heart. That $2.50 she had promised seemed nearer than it had since she reached home.

All the next day they talked over Mother's idea, and in the evening the three children had a practice together, with Mother at the piano. They soon found that they could get along very well with several simple hymns, and this made them full of eagerness to see what they could do outside.

Two evenings later they started out. And what a happy time they did have! Barbara sang as she had never sung at home. She felt she was using her one talent for Jesus. People opened their windows to listen to the clear, musical little voice that rang out on the still evening air. Richard played very well on his violin, and Bessie helped a lot too. She knocked at the doors and told the story of how they were all trying to gather money so that their missionary would not have to be brought back from India. No one could resist her sweet little smile. At every house she received something. One lady gave five cents, another ten cents, and one happy old gentleman brought a quarter out of his trousers pocket.

When at last they all reached home, they were so excited and happy that Mother scarcely knew what to do with them. After counting up their money, they found they had collected ninety-four cents.

"Why!" exclaimed Barbara, "we shall have to go out only three or four times to get more than I promised."

"It's wonderful," said Mother. "I prayed that God would bless you tonight, and I am sure He has. That one talent came in useful, didn't it, Barbara?"

Barbara blushed a little.

"Anyway," she said, "I am glad I shall be able to keep my promise, and have something to give Him after all."

# One Good Turn

*G*OOD-BY, RONNY."

"Good-by, Mother."

"Be a good boy at school today; don't forget."

"I won't," shouted Ronny as he dashed out of the gate and down the road.

As he disappeared and Mother went into the house again, her face clouded over a little.

"I do wish Ronny would be a better boy. He is so very selfish. He always wants everything for himself, and it's so hard to get him to do anything for anyone but himself. I wonder what I can do to make him different!"

That afternoon, just after dinner, Ronny joined in a baseball game in the field near the school. It was a fast, rough game, with lots of good pitching and hard hitting. At last it came Ronny's turn to bat.

There was nothing he loved so much as a game of ball, and to hold a bat in his hand was the height of happiness. Proudly he walked to the plate. Carefully he watched the first ball, and with one mighty hit sent

69

it right over to the wall of the playground, but it was a foul.

The next ball came across. Flushed with his first effort, he swung again, fully intending this time to send the ball clear over the wall into the street, and so make a name for himself the boys would never forget.

But suddenly something went wrong. Ronny could never tell just what it was. He thought he swung too quick and was hit by the ball. What Ronny did know was that he suddenly felt a sharp pain in his forehead.

As he put up his hand he felt something wet and sticky. Poor Ronny turned very pale and dropped the bat.

"I'm afraid I'll have to go in," he said turning toward the school.

The boys crowded around him and helped him to a chair in one of the classrooms.

"I'll be all right," he said to the others; "you go on with the game." With that they left him.

But Ronny did not feel all right. He felt very sick. He wished with all his heart that he were at home, and that Mother would come and bathe his forehead.

Just then one of the senior boys looked into the room.

"Hello, what's the matter?" he asked in a kindly voice. "Hurt yourself?"

"A little," said Ronny, trying to look brave. "Ball caught me on the forehead."

"That's too bad. Better come along with me. I'll bathe it for you if you'll let me."

"Thanks," said Ronny. "It is looking pretty bad, isn't it?"

"Oh, we'll soon have that all right," said the senior boy. "This isn't so bad as having your head knocked off, is it?"

"No," said Ronny, smiling despite the pain.

They went into the cloakroom and there, with a tenderness equaled only by mother herself, the senior boy bathed the wound and bound it up with liniment from the school first-aid outfit. Then with a jolly laugh and a "Cheerio!" he bade Ronny good-by and rushed off to his next class.

When Ronny reached home that night he had a great story to tell.

"But wasn't he nice?" he exclaimed. "You know, Mom, I'd never spoken to him before. I can't understand why he should have been so kind to a stranger. And he is one of the big boys, you know."

"It was good of him, indeed," said Mother. "I appreciate it ever so much. You will tell him so, won't you? It was a kind thing to do. I hope you will always be as thoughtful, Ronny."

"Oh, I couldn't be as good as that," sighed Ronny.

Two days passed. Again it was evening. Ronny was due home at half-past four. But he did not come. Five o'clock passed, and still no Ronny. Mother began to get angry. Then she grew anxious.

At half-past five, when Mother was just about to telephone to the police station, Ronny turned up.

Mother was waiting for him on the doorstep.

"Ronny," she said severely, "what do you mean by coming home at this hour? Don't you know how late it is? I really can't allow——"

"It's all right, Mom, I—I—I had to walk home."

"Walk home!" said Mother in astonishment. "Walk home, indeed! Don't you have your nickel for your bus fare? I know I gave it to you this morning before you left."

"I know, Mom," said Ronny, a twinkle coming in his eye. "You gave me the nickel all right, but I gave it away to one of the boys."

"Gave it away!" cried Mother, more astonished still. "What for?"

"I just couldn't help it," said Ronny. "You see I—er—I met one of the little boys—you know, out of the baby's class, we call it—just as I was going to get on the bus. He looked very pale and sick, so I asked him what was the matter. He said he didn't feel well enough to walk

home, and he had lost his nickel. So, well, there was nothing else to do. I—er—well—I just gave him mine and walked instead. And here I am."

"O you darling boy!" cried Mother, throwing her arms around Ronny's neck and dropping some tears down the back of his new sweater.

"Why, what's the matter, Mom? It's nothing like what that boy did for me the other day. It's nothing at all. Really it isn't."

"O Ronny," said Mother, smiling through her tears, "it's just everything to me."

# When the Guards Saluted

*I* SAW AN UNUSUAL
sight in Rome some time ago. It happened at the Tomb
of the Unknown Warrior.

After the first world war, as your daddy has probably told you, each nation in the conflict took one of
the dead men from the battlefield, someone so badly
hurt that he could not be recognized, someone without
a number or a name, and buried him with great honor,
surpassing that given to princes and generals. This was
to show that they were grateful for all the sufferings
of the millions of poor, common, unknown people who
had to do the fighting and the dying.

Probably you have seen the Tomb of the Unknown
Soldier at Arlington, or in Westminster Abbey, or
under the Arc de Triomphe in Paris, where a flame
is kept constantly burning in his memory.

But it is about the one in Rome I especially want
to tell you now. It is in the center of the city, and is
part of a very beautiful and very massive, stately monument. Giant wreaths decorate the spot, and two soldiers,
fully armed, stand on guard.

As I watched these two soldiers for a few minutes,
I noticed something very unusual. They saluted everybody who passed, men, women, and little children—
all, in fact, who saluted the honored dead whose tomb
they guarded.

Forward and backward went their rifles as people
mounted the steps, saluted, and passed by. I was afraid
they would get mixed up sometimes and fail to salute
in unison—and they surely did; but in a moment they
recovered themselves and continued their strangely
beautiful task.

Naturally, I was particularly interested in the children who had come to honor the dead hero. Would the
two stern guards recognize their salute also?

Yes. They did. And the children, who didn't understand very well, I think, what it all meant, seemed to enjoy it. Fancy being able to make a real, live soldier, with a big gun and a bayonet in his hand, salute you! The boys and girls all took full advantage of the opportunity. And as they walked, arms raised, before the sentries, up would go the guns, and the children would look *very* pleased with themselves.

Only one was disappointed. She was just a tiny little girl, about two and a half, I should say, dressed in a pretty pink frock, and she held up her hand again and again, but all in vain. Perhaps she was so very little that the guards did not see her. Anyhow, they didn't return her salute, and she went down the steps again with her Daddy, feeling very sorry for herself. I felt sorry for her, too.

I wondered what would happen if a foreigner went by; so I crossed in front and raised my arm like the others. (For though I hate war, I honor all men who suffer and die for some great ideal.) Up went the guns again, and I began to understand why the children liked to go by so often.

As I thought about it afterward, it seemed to me that those two soldiers were really doing what the poor dead man behind them would like to do could he see all the world coming to do him honor. They were responding on his behalf, and because he was just a poor, unknown man, one of the common people, they saluted

everybody, poor and rich, young and old, friend and stranger.

I think that is how we should act also, don't you? We are to do what Somebody else would do if He were here. As Paul once said, "We are ambassadors for Christ"—we are "in Christ's stead."

So just as Jesus loved everybody and was kind to all, we too are to have the same friendly spirit. Not just talking to the boys and girls who have plenty of money, or who have some influential relatives, or who can do us some service in return, but being friendly and courteous to all, whoever they may be, whatever their name or station.

And, of course, unlike those two guards at the tomb, *we* must never overlook the tiniest of little ones, however small they be, who look up to us for help or guidance, or just a kindly greeting. For them especially, best beloved of Heaven, we must ever have a tender watchcare and a smile of love.

# How John Saved His Daddy

*A*FTER READING IN *Bedtime Stories,* volume 3, about the wonderful way in which children's prayers have been answered, an old friend of mine sent me the following thrilling story:

With her husband and little son she lives in a very lonely section of New South Wales, Australia. Some distance from the tiny farmhouse runs a river which, usually calm and well-behaved, sometimes, after heavy rain, overflows its banks and does a lot of damage.

Well, it had been raining and raining for days, and little John was beginning to wonder whether the sun would ever shine again. Father, too, was very anxious, for he knew what so much rain might mean. All this time the river was rising nearer and nearer to the top of its banks. Would the rain stop before the water came over?

If Mother were only at home, thought John and his Daddy. Somehow things always seemed brighter then; but she wasn't, having gone away to nurse a sick friend. So the two were all alone, waiting, watching, wondering, and hoping.

All of a sudden Daddy raised a cry.

"Look! It's over the top!"

It was. Though the surging flood was half a mile away, they could see it rushing toward them.

The cattle, the sheep, the chickens! what would happen to them as the waters surged by?

There was not a moment to lose.

"Stay on the veranda!" cried Father to John. "I'll be back in a minute."

And off he dashed in a desperate effort to reach the barns.

Crash! Splash! The water had reached the farmhouse and swept beyond it.

John stood on the veranda, breathless with excitement, and very much frightened.

Where was Daddy? What had happened to him?

Ah, there he was! He could see him now, with the water up to his waist, and it was rising every moment.

But look! He was off his feet, floundering in the water, being fast swept away in the awful torrent, with cows and chickens and the driftwood from many barns and houses, smashed to pieces farther up the river.

John was helpless, terrified.

Then in that awful moment he remembered Jesus, and how Mother had taught him to pray "in every time of need."

Could Jesus help now?

"Jesus!" he cried frantically. "Jesus! Don't let Daddy drown! Please, please, don't let Daddy drown!"

He wrung his hands, and tears started to his eyes.

Then a strange thing happened. You may smile at it, but it is true.

At that very moment, when all seemed lost, a long-handled pitchfork, of all things, came floating toward the spot where Daddy was fighting desperately for his life. Eagerly he grabbed it, and driving it deep into the ground, held on till the  worst of the flood had passed. Then, making his way to a fence, the top of which was just sticking up above the water, he managed at last to find his way back home.

Was John glad to see him safe and sound? I should say so!

"Just an accident, a happen so," I can hear someone whisper.

Well, John doesn't think so, nor does his Daddy or his Mummy. They think it was just another evidence that "the angel of the Lord encampeth round about them that fear Him, and delivereth them" (Psalms 34:7), and that Jesus loves to hear little boys pray and to answer their prayers.

# Back From the Sea

NELLIE AND FRANKIE were on their way to the beach for the afternoon. How happy they were! There was nothing they loved so much as playing in the sand or paddling in the warm, shallow water.

"Now let me remind you both of just one thing," said Daddy as the car slowed down. "Remember that you are both wearing new shoes. Take them off as soon as you get on the beach, and be very careful not to lose them."

"Yes, Daddy!" they cried. "We will." But their thoughts were far away—on the beautiful wavelets which were breaking softly on the shore.

The car stopped, the door opened, and out jumped the two excited children, who ran off toward the water at top speed.

As they reached the sand, Nellie remembered about her shoes, and taking them off, carefully laid them where she was sure she would be able to find them again. Frankie, however, in his eagerness to reach the

ocean, quite forgot all about his promise until he was right down near the water. Then because he thought it was too far to go back, he just kicked off his shoes and socks, left them where they fell, and dashed on in.

What a wonderful time they had together! When they had paddled long enough, they built sand castles, ran races, then paddled some more. So busy were they with their play that they failed to notice the turn of the tide, or how the waves crept slowly but surely up the beach to where Frankie's precious new shoes were lying. But the waves came on just the same.

By and by, all too soon, Daddy called from far up the beach, "It's time to go home; we'll have to be going soon."

Then began the search for the shoes. Nellie found hers all right, because she had been careful to leave them in a safe place. But Frankie's shoes were nowhere to be found. In fact, he couldn't even find the place where he had left them. It was covered by the water!

They searched and searched, but it was no use. The shoes were not to be found. Daddy said that Frankie was a very careless little boy, and he would have to go home barefooted. But Nellie said that she had a pair of slippers in the car and Frankie could wear them.

So that is how they returned home. Nellie in her shiny new shoes and Frankie in Nellie's slippers.

Frankie did not feel very happy about it, for he liked new shoes just as much as Nellie. And you can be quite sure that Daddy did not feel happy about it, nor Mother either, for they would have to find the money for another pair.

"Maybe we could go back in the morning," said Daddy, "and have another look."

"What's the use?" said Mother. "They will have been washed out in the ocean by now."

"Well, we might as well go," said Daddy. "It won't do any harm to look once more."

So in the morning they all drove back to the beach again to search for Frankie's shoes.

This time, strangely enough, it was Daddy and Mother who got out of the car, while Nellie and Frankie remained inside. They said they wanted to stay behind a little while by themselves, but didn't say why. This was so unusual that Daddy said they could if they wished; then he and Mother started off without them.

Left alone, Nellie and Frankie knelt down by the back seat of the car and began to pray. Nellie, by the way, was just nine and Frankie, seven. But they believed that Jesus loves children and delights to help them when they get into trouble.

So together they sent up a little prayer that Frankie's lost shoes might be found! Six times they prayed the same prayer, over and over again.

Then they saw Daddy and Mother hurrying back to the car. They were smiling happily as though they had had good fortune.

They had.

"Look!" cried Nellie. "See what Daddy has!"

"My shoes! My shoes!" cried Frankie.

Yes, there they were, and hardly damaged at all.

Daddy had found them not a hundred yards from where he had stopped the car. How or why they happened to be just there, no one could tell, but everybody was thankful, especially Nellie and Frankie, who then told what they had been doing while Daddy and Mother were on the beach searching for the shoes.

Such a little thing to pray for, you say? I know. Just a pair of shoes! But why not? Jesus is interested in all the little things of our lives. Did He not say of the sparrow: "Not one of them is forgotten before God"? He did, and He added, too: "Ye are of more value than many sparrows." Luke 12:6, 7.

So we are not to hesitate to pray for little things as well as for big things. Not one of our prayers—not a single one—is "forgotten before God."

# Katie, Chris, and the Christmas Tree

*I*T WAS THE DAY before Christmas, and still there was no Christmas tree in its usual corner in the dining room.

Katie and Chris had crept into the room day after day, hoping to see it there as they had in years gone by, but the corner was always empty. They waited and waited, expecting to find it there any minute, only to be disappointed every time they looked.

Now it was the very last day. They felt they couldn't wait any longer. They just had to ask Mother about it, and so they did.

"Mamma," asked Chris, "aren't we going to have a Christmas tree this year?"

"This is Christmas Eve," added Katie.

Mother's face fell. She had dreaded this moment.

"Darlings, I'm so sorry," she said. "I'm afraid we won't have one this year. I asked Daddy to bring us one, but he has been so busy he forgot all about it. He told me so last night, and now it's too late. We live so far from town we never could get one in time."

"O Mamma!" cried Chris. "We do love the pretty tree in the corner. It won't be the same without it."

"It's too bad," said Mamma. "I'll have to make it up to you some other way."

"But we want the tree," said Chris.

"Yes, we want the tree," echoed Katie.

The two children ran away to share their grief. But there was nothing anybody could do about it. At least, it seemed that way.

Then as they talked together, Katie said, "Chris, if we were to tell Jesus about the tree, do you think He would send us one?"

"Maybe He would," said Chris.

So, without telling Mother a word about it, they got

down on their knees and told Jesus what was in their hearts, the thing they wanted most just then.

You may say, Fancy asking Jesus for a Christmas tree! I know. It does sound strange. But Jesus understands little children, and loves to have them tell Him all their hopes and dreams.

He likes to surprise

them, too! I know He does.

That very evening, soon after Katie and Chris had gone to bed, there was a knock on the front door. Who should it be but the neighbor who lived on the farm next to theirs. He had a strange tale to tell.

Coming back from town that very evening, he told Mother he had been stopped by a stranger and asked whether he would take something to the home of Katie and Chris.

"I looked at him carefully," said the neighbor, "and tried to think who it could be; but it was nobody I had seen before; and I have lived here all my life and know everybody for miles around."

"That's strange," said Mother. "But what did he give you to bring us?"

"That's the funny thing," said the neighbor. "He gave me a Christmas tree, of all things; and I'm sure you have one already."

"But we haven't!" cried Mother. "And the children want one so very much. Who could have sent it to us?"

90

"I don't know," said the neighbor, "but here it is, a very beautiful one, too."

At the words "Christmas tree," Katie and Chris—who had been listening hard all the time—came bounding out of bed to where Mother and the neighbor were standing at the front door.

And there was the tree, the biggest and most beautiful Christmas tree they had seen in all their lives.

"Oh!" they cried together. "What a perfectly lovely tree!"

"I knew Jesus would send it!" said Katie.

"I knew He would, too," said Chris.

And Katie told me herself—she and Chris are both grown up now —that all her life she has never forgotten that wonderful night or the thrill she felt as she realized that her prayer had been answered.

# How Ginger Paid His Bill

*H*ERE IS A DELIGHTFUL
little dog story, told me by a friend the other day.

Arriving home late one evening with his wife, he
turned on the light in the hall, and was about to go
upstairs, when he stopped suddenly.

What was that?

Noises!

Their hearts almost stopped beating.

Fancy burglars coming to their home! What should
they do?

Standing very still, they listened fearfully.

The noise continued. Strange! Surely a burglar
would have heard the click of the door, or noticed the
light go on—unless he had found something of unusual value.

My friend decided to explore, and very carefully,
treading softly to avoid the creaks, he crept upstairs.

Ah! A bedroom door opened, and something dark
and big sprang out.

A dog! A big brown retriever.

Investigating further, my friend discovered that the dog had got in through an unfastened window, and had actually slept on the bed for some time, probably having had his slumbers disturbed by the return of the owners.

Whose was he?

Well, it turned out that he had once lived there, and feeling lonely, no doubt, had come back to his old home.

Ginger, as they called him, was given some food, and later, very politely, of course, was shown the door.

But that was not the end of it.

In the morning what should they discover on the top of the stairs but a bag of small cakes!

Who put them there?

Only Ginger could have done it. Was it his strange, doggy way of saying, "Thank you," and paying for his sleep on the bed?

Who can tell? Who will ever know?

What I would like to know, of course, and what I'm sure you would all like to know also, is, Where did Ginger get the cakes?

But perhaps that's not a fair question. His honesty and kindly thoughtfulness lead me to throw a veil of secrecy over what might possibly have been a rash misdeed.

After all, I thought to myself, does not the Bible tell us that love covers a multitude of sins?

# At the Dog Show

*H*AVE YOU EVER BEEN to a dog show? For years and years I have wanted to go to one, and have never seemed to find the time just when the show was on. But this year I went to one, and what a lot of dogs I saw!

Big dogs and little dogs; pretty dogs and ugly dogs; white dogs and black dogs and brown dogs; dogs with long pointed noses; dogs with short stubby noses; dogs with long curly hair; dogs with short straight hair. I really had not imagined there could be so many different kinds of dogs in the world.

I was not there very long, not nearly so long as I should have liked to be, but just long enough to notice one very interesting thing.

It was this:

The dogs had been arranged in two main sections —big dogs on the ground floor and little dogs on the first floor upstairs.

What drew my attention first to this arrangement was the difference in the noise from both places.

Downstairs I could hear the occasional gruff, deep-toned barks and growls from bulldogs, Alsatians, retrievers, and the like. There was something very stolid, very stately, very important, about the sound from the big dogs.

Upstairs, however, it was altogether different. This was surely the noisiest place on earth. Every little dog was having his say, trying to shout louder than all the other little dogs around him.

Yap-yap, yap-yap, yap-yap, yap-yap, yap-yap!

It was simply dreadful. There wasn't a moment's peace and quiet anywhere. They were all at it at once.

It made me wonder whether most boys and girls could not be divided—roughly, anyway—into two such groups.

Some are quiet, solid, and reliable, liking a bit of fun now and then, but going on with the job right away as soon as it is over. This kind of boy or girl thinks a great deal, but doesn't talk too much. He prefers reading a book to telling silly stories. He gives an occasional bark when it is needed, but has no time to "yap."

The others—well, who doesn't know them? They're in the majority, I'm afraid, just as there are far more little dogs than big dogs.

And, oh, how they yap! You hear them on the train, on the streetcar, on the tennis court, or the baseball diamond—everywhere you go.

Yap-yap, yap-yap, yap-yap!

Isn't it tiresome?

They are the sort that quarrel about whether a boy is to be pitcher or batter, or whether another made a run or was touched out, or whether the ball hit the bat or not.

Or, if they are girls, the sort that talk themselves tired about movie stars, or the latest fashion, or the new girl's style of hairdressing.

Oh, I know them, and so do you.

Big dog or little dog, which would you like to be? Do you belong upstairs or down?

ARLO GREER. ARTIST

**Every Day Faithful Jock Ran Beside the Train, Then Stopped and Dashed After
the Newspaper That Was Thrown Out to Him From the Last Coach**

# Faithful Jock

ALKING ABOUT DOGS reminds me of one I saw this summer in a most unexpected place. I'll call him Jock, for, though I tried hard, I never found out his real name.

I was traveling over that long, long trail from the Pacific Coast to Chicago. The train was climbing the western slopes of the Rocky Mountains at the time, round and round, twist and turn, up and up, many thousand feet above the sea.

One mighty desolation it is, with an awful grandeur of its own. For miles and miles the train hurtles on with never a sign of human habitation, unless perhaps the tiny shack of a lonely rancher, or a group of railway workers beside the track.

No man's land it is in very truth.

And then—a dog!

I could hardly believe my eyes, and leaned out of the window to make sure. Yes, there he was, a fine black retriever, running at top speed beside the train!

Where did he live? Why was he there? Did he want the train to stop and take him on board?

Then an interesting thing happened. From the very last coach a newspaper was thrown out by somebody. Instantly the dog stopped, turned, and dashed after it, as though anxious to learn the latest news of the outside world.

A porter came to the window where I was standing, and as we watched the fast-receding form of the dog, I asked whether he knew anything about him.

"Yes," said the porter, "that is the most faithful dog I have ever known. He belongs to a man who lives in that little hut over yonder, and for years now, winter and summer, he has met this train to pick up his master's paper. Winter or summer, he never fails, and we expect him here as regularly as the sunrise."

"But how about the winter snows, when you have to run a snowplow in front of the train?" I asked.

"It makes no difference to him. Snow or rain or hail, he is always here on time. In fact, if he weren't, we'd wonder what had happened."

Faithful Jock! Bless his dear old courageous heart!

Do you wonder that I leaned out of the window once more to catch one last glimpse of his shining black coat as he disappeared down the bank in the gloaming?

# Heard on the Beach

"*G*O AWAY!" "YOU CAN'T play here." "This is our pond." "Go away!"

I looked up. Not far away I saw two little boys standing in a pool of water on which were floating a number of tiny boats.

Near them was a third boy, a very little fellow, in fact, but evidently one with lots of determination behind his sweet chubby face. In his hand was a piece of wood shaped like a ship, which he called his "Keena Mary," and this he intended to sail upon the other boys' pool. He stepped in.

"Go away!"

This time there was anger in the tone.

But the Very Little Boy did not understand. Anyhow, it made no difference.

"Keena Mary" was duly floated.

"Will you go away!"

At this moment the Very Little Boy's Daddy appeared from somewhere, and taking him by the hand, tried very hard to lead him away from the older boys to where he would be more welcome.

Alas! The Very Little Boy did not want to go. He could not understand why he could not float his boat in the other little boys' pool, nor why they should not want him to play with them; so he lifted up his voice and wept.

Boo-hoo-hoo!

What a howl it was! It must have been heard all over the beach, perhaps even on the top of the cliffs.

Boo-hoo-hoo-hoo! Boo-hoo-hoo-hoo!

So many tears ran down his cheeks that his face looked like Niagara Falls. I had never seen such a picture of despair.

Then a beautiful thing happened.

Another Daddy appeared on the scene, and whispered something in the ear of the biggest little boy in the pool, whose name, I learned, was John.

There was a brief discussion; but in a moment or two I saw John leave the pool and walk up the beach to where the Very Little Boy was still weeping bitterly.

Taking him by the hand, John led him to the pool, and told him he could play there if he wished, after all.

In a moment the tear-stained face was wreathed in smiles, and the beach rang again with happy laughter. Together the two went paddling in the water, and soon the "Keena Mary" was afloat once more.

What a fine thing John did that afternoon! I hope someday he will read this story and see that somebody saw his sweet, unselfish deed and told the whole wide world about it.

And I believe the guardian angels—who watch over all little boys—saw it also, and so it went all over heaven too. How very far a kindly deed will go!

# Geoffrey's Bandsmen

*I*T HAPPENED ON THE way back from the band. That is, I mean the quarrel happened then.

As a special treat, Geoffrey and his sister Anne had been taken to hear the band one evening.

They loved going to the band, and would promise their Daddy that they would be good as angels for weeks if only he would take them there.

Of course, as soon as the music was over they usually forgot all about their promises.

Well, the band was over one night, and Daddy, Geoffrey, and Anne had started to walk home. Unfortunately, both children wanted to hold Daddy's right hand. A very silly thing, of course, for surely Daddy's left hand was just as comfortable to hold as his right hand. But then most quarrels start over very silly little things.

"I was there first," said Geoffrey.

"No, you weren't; I was," said Anne.

"I was; you get away," said Geoffrey.

104

"I was; you get away," retorted Anne.

"What does it matter?" asked Daddy.

"I had your right hand first," said Geoffrey.

"No; I did," said Anne. "Anyway, it's my turn."

"No, it isn't."

"It is."

"It isn't."

"Stop it, children!" cried Daddy in desperation. "What will the people think of you both, making all this fuss at this time of night?"

"It's my place," said Geoffrey, taking no notice, and trying still harder to push Anne away.

"It isn't yours; it's mine," cried Anne, holding on to Daddy's hand still more tightly.

"Will you stop it, Geoffrey?" said Daddy firmly. "Come round and take my other hand at once."

"Don't want to," said Geoffrey sulkily, suddenly dropping behind. "I'll walk by myself then."

"All right," replied

Daddy. "And we shall not forget this next band night."

So the procession moved toward home, with Geoffrey dropping farther and farther behind, and shuffling his feet along in a manner that must have made the angels weep.

It was long past bedtime when they were all indoors, and Mamma hurried the children up to bed without making too many inquiries as to what had happened.

Geoffrey was soon between the sheets, and it was not long before he dropped off into a troubled slumber.

Hello! What was this? He was at the band again. Surely it could not be! But he was. And to his utter amazement, he was the conductor. Behind him were hundreds of people, many of whom he recognized. Lots of boys from his school were there too. He felt very proud of himself. Fancy being the conductor of the band in front of all his school friends. My! wouldn't they all like to be in his shoes? He made up his mind that he would make their very ears tingle with the wonderful music he would bring from the band that night.

Then he looked around at his bandsmen. Yes, they were all there. Were they ready to play? Yes. He tapped his baton smartly on the music holder, and swelled up with pride. But nobody moved.

He tapped again. No one seemed to take the slightest notice.

"Start!" he shouted. "Can't you hear me? Start!"

At this the drummer banged his drum and the man with the trombone blew one great long note. The people behind him laughed. He could hear his school friends tittering.

"Play!" he cried again. "Start! All of you start!"

He tapped furiously on the music holder.

The man with the piccolo blew a piercing blast and stopped. Then the cornets began, but they all seemed to be playing different tunes. Geoffrey was in despair. He waved his arms in an endeavor to beat time, but there was no time. Rather, there were all sorts of time. The clarinets had begun now, all on different notes. Geoffrey shouted to them to look at their music, but they took no notice. Now all the rest of the players began, and the confusion became terrible. It seemed as if each one was playing a tune of his own. No one took any notice of anybody but himself. Geoffrey could hear "Three Blind Mice" and "Home Sweet Home" and "Old Man River" and "America" all mixed up together. Every man was playing just what he liked and how he liked and in any time he liked.

As for Geoffrey, the players took no notice of him whatever. He might as well not have been there. And yet he felt that he was responsible. The people behind him were expecting great things of him. And this was all he could do! It was terrible, and as the din increased, Geoffrey became frantic.

"Stop!" he shrieked at them all. "Stop! Stop it, I say! Can't you hear me? Do what you're told, will you! Oh, why don't you listen to me? Stop! Stop, I say! Stop!"

"There, there," said Mamma, putting her hand on his head. "It's all right, dear; don't worry any more."

Geoffrey sat bolt upright in bed.

"So I'm not at the band, after all," he said.

"At the band?" laughed Daddy. "You're right here in bed."

"Oh!" said Geoffrey. "You should have heard them. They just wouldn't do what I told them, Daddy. They were so obstinate. They just played their own tunes as loud as they could, and wouldn't take a bit of notice when I shouted at them."

"Who?" asked Daddy.

"The bandsmen, of course. Didn't you hear the noise?"

"Well, no, I can't say that I did," said Daddy. "I heard a noise, and I also heard someone acting like that on the way back from the band last night."

"Oh—er—yes," said Geoffrey, waking up fully at last. "I wonder if that's why I dreamed that dreadful dream."

"I should think it was," said Daddy.

"Well, of all things," said Geoffrey as he dropped back on his pillow and went to sleep.

Geoffrey's dream was not forgotten in the morning, and Daddy found it very useful later on when the old trouble began to come back again.

For whenever Geoffrey showed any signs of grumpiness or disobedience after that, all Daddy had to say was, "How about your bandsmen, Geoffrey?"

It always had a wonderful effect!

**Muriel Was Tired Playing Store With Her Dolls; Then Came Kitty, Her First Customer. Delighted, She Gave Him a Drink of Milk**

# Muriel's Customer

*L*ITTLE MURIEL WAS A very lonely girl. Her Mother had been taken very ill and sent to a hospital, and she had come to stay with her auntie.

She liked being with her auntie all right, but there was no one to play with. Auntie was getting old and seemed to have forgotten that she had ever been a child herself. Muriel was sure she didn't understand little girls. She was always saying, "Please do be quiet, Muriel," and "Don't get into mischief, Muriel," until poor Muriel didn't know just what to do to be good.

One day auntie got an idea. "When I was a little girl," she said, "we used to play store."

"I'd like to play store," said Muriel, glad to find something at last that auntie thought was "being good."

So auntie allowed Muriel to take some wooden boxes out into the garden and some old cans that had once contained such goodies as taffy and fruit.

For a little while Muriel was very happy arranging the counter, but when that was done, she began to be

111

lonesome again, for what is the good of a store if there is no one to buy your goods?

So she got one of her old dolls and stuck it up in front of the counter, and pretended that the doll was a customer. But a doll is a very unsatisfactory sort of customer. For one thing she will not take the things away, and for another she will not pay for them. So poor Muriel soon got tired of that, and dismissed the doll from the store.

"Oh dear!" she sighed. "I do wish someone would come to play with me!"

Hardly had she spoken when a nice tabby cat walked slowly around the corner of the store, and jumped up on a box in front of the counter.

112

"Well, you are a nice customer!" said Muriel, smiling for the first time that afternoon. "And what would you like to buy today, Mr. Pussycat?"

"A penny's worth of sugar," said Mr. Pussycat as well as he could, opening his mouth wide and getting rather too near the sugar bag for safety.

Muriel guessed what he meant, and held up a piece of sugar to see if she had guessed rightly.

Mr. Pussycat opened his mouth wider still and swallowed the lump of sugar with relish. Evidently Muriel had not been mistaken.

"But now, Mr. Pussycat, how about paying for it?" said Muriel sternly. "Nobody is allowed to take things from this store without paying for them, you know."

Mr. Pussycat raised his right foot as if about to pass over the necessary money, and Muriel took the will for the deed.

Well, they had great times together. So long as

the supply of sugar lasted, Mr. Pussycat was a regular customer, and Muriel succeeded in selling him quite a number of other things as well. He came back the next day, and they started all over again.

Muriel got a bright idea, and decided to enlarge her store and add a dairy. Mr. Pussycat strongly approved, and came back frequently to purchase saucerfuls of milk. The only trouble was to get auntie to understand why so much milk was needed in the shop.

So in a very little while Muriel and Mr. Pussycat became great friends. He would follow her about everywhere she went, and even when auntie took her out shopping Mr. Pussycat would follow behind like a little dog. They played together all day long, and in her love for pussy Muriel forgot her loneliness.

Then one day a letter came to say that Mother was better and Muriel could go home again. She didn't know whether to laugh for joy at the thought of going home or cry for sadness at parting from her new-found friend.

So she played one last game of store and sold Mr. Pussycat all the milk he could drink and all the sugar he could eat, and didn't charge him anything for it either. Then she said good-by with tears running down her cheeks.

Auntie said it was very foolish for a little girl to cry over a cat, especially when she ought to be so thankful

that her Mother was better, but Muriel just couldn't help it.

Soon she was home again, and so glad to see her Mamma well and strong once more. But somehow she couldn't forget her friend, and longed to have him with her always.

Then one morning, what do you suppose happened?

Well, it was her birthday, and when she got downstairs she saw a strange-looking parcel beside her plate on the breakfast table. Quickly she removed the paper. Underneath was a basket, and in the basket was—

Mr. Pussycat.

So auntie had understood after all!

# Kidnaped!

*H*AVE YOU EVER WON-
dered what it would be like to be kidnaped? Perhaps
you have asked yourself just what you would do if a
stranger suddenly picked you up and hurried you away
in his car. Well, here is the story of a little boy who had
this experience. I know it is true, for his Mother wrote
and told me all about it.

I am going to call him Raymond, for, of course, he
wouldn't want me to use his real name.

He was just six years old at the time this happened,
but though he was very young, he loved to do what he
called his "missionary work." That is, when the minister at his church said that he needed money to send
to the missionaries in foreign lands, Raymond would
set out bravely to call at the neighbors' homes and tell
them all about it. It was really surprising how much
money he would bring home sometimes.

One day, in the summer of 1942, Raymond had
been out collecting his "missionary money." He was
almost finished. As he was walking home along a

country road he suddenly heard a car slow down and stop beside him. A strange man put his head out of the window and asked Raymond if he wanted a ride.

"No, thank you," said Raymond, remembering his Mother's strict warning that he was never to accept a ride from a stranger.

"Oh, come on," said the man.

"Thank you; I'd rather walk," said Raymond. "I do not have very far to go."

The stranger opened the door and got out.

"Get in there," he ordered, picking Raymond up bodily and shoving him on the front seat.

"But I don't want to ride!" shouted Raymond. "Let me out!"

It was no use. Already the door was shut and the

man was starting the car. Soon they were moving rapidly along the road.

"What's your name?" asked the stranger.

"Raymond."

"Who's your father?"

Raymond told him.

"How much money does he earn?"

"Don't know," said Raymond. And at the mention of money he became more frightened, for he remembered the "missionary money" in his pocket which he had gathered that very afternoon. He hoped this bad man would not find out about it.

Now the car was speeding past his home, and Raymond saw all the old familiar places being left behind.

"Oh, dear!" he thought, "where is he going to take me?"

Then he remembered that Mother had said that if he was working for Jesus, he need never be afraid, for the angels would surely look after him. So he began to say a little prayer; but he was so frightened that he said it out loud.

"What was that you were saying?" asked the man.

"I was asking Jesus to save me," said Raymond, as the tears rolled down his cheeks.

"Oh, very well, then, very well," said the man, putting his foot on the brake. "Get out; get out!"

With that he stopped the car, opened the door, and pushed Raymond onto the grass at the side of the road. Then he jumped in again, and the car roared away into the distance.

As Raymond stood there wondering what to do next, a woman from a near-by farm came up to him and asked, "What in the world are you doing all alone out here?"

Raymond told her all that had happened. Getting her own car, she soon hurried him back to his Mother.

Mother said he was a very brave boy, but Raymond said he was quite sure all the time that Jesus would help him because of the "missionary money" he had in his pocket that afternoon.

I think He did, too, don't you?

# Grandma's Piano

**R**UTH JUST LOVED TO stay at her grandma's house, for she always had a happy time there. Grandma was kind and good to her, telling her stories, mending her dolly's clothes, and of course, giving her nice things to eat.

Every Wednesday night grandma would put Ruth to bed early, then walk across town to Mrs. Henderson's house to attend prayer meeting. Except for illness or a very bad storm, grandma had not missed a prayer meeting in twenty years; and even now that she was "getting on in years," as she said, she was determined to be there, come what might.

One day, while Ruth and grandma were having a jolly little chat together, Ruth asked a question which seemed to puzzle the old lady quite a bit.

"Grandma," asked Ruth, "why do you have to go all the way to Mrs. Henderson's house for the prayer meeting? It's too far for you to walk nowadays."

"Well, darling," said grandma, "I don't think I have ever thought about it. We've all been going to

120

Mrs. Henderson's house for years and years, and I suppose I shall keep on going there as long as I live."

"But, Grandma," persisted Ruth, "why don't you have the prayer meeting in your house? Then you wouldn't have to walk anywhere!"

"I suppose I never stopped to think about it," said grandma, smiling. "Oh, yes, I did. I know. It's because I don't have a piano, and Mrs. Henderson does. So there you are, dear, that's the reason."

But if grandma thought that Ruth would be satisfied with that, she was mistaken.

"Grandma," said the little girl after a while, "why don't you have a piano in your house?"

"Because," said grandma, "I don't really need a piano. I could still play it, though, if I had one."

"But, Grandma," said Ruth, "you really do need one; then you wouldn't have to go out in the cold and wet; and you wouldn't have to walk so far."

"I know, darling," said grandma, "but there's another reason—and a very important one, too. I couldn't afford to buy a piano if I wanted one. I think we had better leave things just as they are."

"But, Grandma," said Ruth, "couldn't Jesus give you a piano?"

"Of course He could," said grandma; "but I don't think He will because—well, as I told you, I don't really need one."

"But, Grandma, you do need one," said Ruth, "and I am going to ask Jesus to send you one. Won't it be lovely when you have a piano of your very own, and the people all come here to the prayer meeting?"

Grandma smiled and sighed. She did not know what to say now. Not for a million dollars would she destroy Ruth's faith in the power and love of Jesus.

"Well, dear," she said finally, "we must leave it all to Him, mustn't we?"

"Oh, yes, Grandma," said Ruth. "Of course we

must, but I am going to ask Him to send you one."

And she did.

Morning by morning, and evening by evening she sent up the sweet and loving petition, "Please, Jesus, send grandma a piano, so she won't have to go so far to the prayer meeting."

I don't know exactly how long it was before the answer came—maybe two or three weeks, maybe a month. Then one afternoon, as grandma and Ruth were sitting together in the dining room and grandma was putting a stitch or two in Ruth's dolly, they were suddenly aroused by strange sounds outside the door.

Some men were shouting to each other.

"Heave ho!" cried one. "Steady there," cried another. "Steady now. Take it easy, men. Take it easy."

Then the men seemed to be climbing the stairs to the front door, coming ever closer and closer.

Grandma stopped her work and looked up. "What is that?" she asked. "Who can be coming to see us this afternoon?"

"Steady now," came the voices again. "Take it easy. Let her down carefully. Don't let her fall. Careful now, careful."

Then there was a loud bang on the front door.

Ruth's eyes sparkled with excitement.

"Grandma!" she cried. "Perhaps it's your piano. Oh, Grandma, let's go and see!"

Ruth flew across the room and opened the door. "Grandma! It is! Jesus has sent your piano."

"I don't know who sent it," said one of the men; "but here it is, and what are we to do with it?"

"Bring it in; bring it in!" said Ruth, while grandma stood back wondering what all this might mean, but with a little prayer of thankfulness in her heart.

They found out afterward that the piano had belonged to one of the prayer meeting ladies who was leaving town and who, not knowing what to do with it, had suddenly had the idea of sending it to grandma.

So here it was at last! A real piano! Right in grandma's own house! No matter who sent it, or why, Ruth was absolutely sure that it had come in answer to her prayer. Grandma said she believed it had, too.

# In the Mirror

*H*AVE YOU EVER
noticed that when you look in a mirror, your hands—
if you are a boy—instinctively go to your tie, to pull it
straight?

If you're a girl, they probably go to your hair, to
pat it into shape, you know.

I suppose that's because we really do want to look
as neat and tidy as possible, and the mirror shows us
what's out of place.

It doesn't have to be a glass mirror, either. A very
calm lake will do just as well. Maybe you have seen
some. There is a much-advertised Mirror Lake in California, and it certainly is pretty, the mountains and
trees being perfectly reflected in the water. But there
are many others. Long ago I saw one in the highlands
of Scotland, and the reflection was wonderful.

There are other kinds of mirrors, too.

Perhaps you are the proud possessor of a watch. If you are, then next time you pass a very big clock that you are sure always has the right time, notice what you do.

Of course, you will look at your watch and compare it with the great big clock, and if they don't agree, you will turn the hands of your watch until they do. That's like looking in a mirror, isn't it? Only you put the watch's tie straight instead of your own.

Then there is another kind of mirror—the law of God. So the Bible says. (James 1:23-25.)

But how can the Ten Commandments be a mirror?

Just think for a moment.

You do something that is questionable,

### THE LAW

**I**

Thou shalt have no other gods before Me.

**II**

Thou shalt not make unto thee any graven image, or any likeness of anything that is in heaven above, or that is in the earth beneath, or that is in the water under the earth: thou shalt not bow down thyself to them, nor serve them: for I the Lord thy God am a jealous God, visiting the iniquity of the fathers upon the children unto the third and fourth generation of them that hate Me; and showing mercy unto thousands of them that love Me, and keep My commandments.

**III**

Thou shalt not take the name of the Lord thy God in vain; for the Lord will not hold him guiltless that taketh His name in vain.

**IV**

Remember the Sabbath day, to keep it holy. Six days shalt thou labor, and do all thy work: but the seventh day is the Sabbath of the Lord thy God: in it thou shalt not do any work, thou, nor thy son, nor thy daughter, thy manservant, nor thy maidservant, nor thy cattle, nor thy stranger that is within thy gates: for in six days the Lord made heaven and earth, the sea, and all that in them is, and rested the seventh day: wherefore the Lord blessed the Sabbath day, and

### OF GOD

**V**

Honor thy father and thy mother: that thy days may be long upon the land which the Lord thy God giveth thee.

**VI**

Thou shalt not kill.

**VII**

Thou shalt not commit adultery.

**VIII**

Thou shalt not steal.

**IX**

Thou shalt not bear false witness against thy neighbor.

**X**

Thou shalt not covet thy neighbor's house, thou shalt not covet thy neighbor's wife, nor his manservant, nor his maidservant, nor his ox, nor his ass, nor anything that is thy neighbor's.

something that you feel is wrong, but you are not quite sure. Then you look at the Ten Commandments, that wonderful, divine mirror; and conscience tells you at once that there is something out of place—something about you that needs to be put straight.

And put it straight you must, though you cannot do that yourself. As soon as you see that there is something wrong with you, then you must ask the dear Lord Jesus to help you make it right. That may mean begging somebody's pardon for saying rude things, or giving back something you have taken that does not belong to you, or correcting a false story you have thoughtlessly passed on. Whatever it is, He will help you do it, for, as the Good Book says, "If we confess our sins, He is faithful and just to forgive us our sins, and to cleanse us from all unrighteousness." 1 John 1:9.

Then you will be able to look in the mirror again and see that all is well—until the next time.

Ah, that is the worst of it, there is always a next time; we keep having to go back to the mirror, don't we? But one day, by the grace of God, we shall have become so like Jesus that to look in His mirror will bring us no regrets.

Then, too, we shall be mirrors also, for He, looking at us, will see a perfect reflection of Himself!

How wonderful!

May that happy day soon dawn for us all.

# The Treasure Hunt

*I*T HAD BEEN A DREARY, wet afternoon, with the rain coming down in bucketfuls. And from the way it was still coming down, the children thought it would go on raining forever and ever.

Everybody was about as miserable as he could be, and a bit short-tempered, too, if the truth must be told.

The children had played every game they could think of, and now there just didn't seem to be anything else to do.

It was when the atmosphere was getting as gloomy inside as it was outside that Mother came in with one of her bright ideas.

"I'll tell you what," she said cheerfully, "let's have a treasure hunt."

There was a chorus of approval.

"Good idea!" shouted Wilfred. "What shall we hunt?"

"Will there be a prize?" cried Sylvia.

"Anything for a change," gasped Gilbert from his seat on the sofa. "Let's start."

128

"I want to hunt, too," cried baby. "Let me hunt, Mamma."

"All in good time," said Mother. "Now listen. I have buried a treasure somewhere in this house, and I'm going to give you fifteen minutes to find it. The one who finds it will have first choice of all the cakes on the table at suppertime."

"Good!" said Wilfred. "I'm going to find it then."

"But what is it like?" asked Sylvia. "We don't know anything about it yet."

"Well," said Mother mysteriously, "it's not very small and it's not very big."

"But that's not enough. We might bring anything," said Gilbert.

"I know," Mother went on. "But this particular object is the most valuable thing in the house, and you have to think what this is before you begin to look."

"Um," said Wilfred frowning. "What can it be? I didn't think there was anything very valuable in this house. Is it the old grandfather clock?"

4-9

"No!" said Mother, "of course not, and please don't try to bring that in here. And I'll tell you this: It's more than an inch square and less than a foot square. It is not locked, but when you open it, you will find lots of valuable things inside."

"Oh, I can't imagine what it is!" exclaimed Gilbert, lazily.

"Think, then," said Mother. "I'm going to start counting in just a minute from now. And mind, if you look in any cupboards or drawers, you must leave everything exactly as you find it. If you don't, you'll lose the prize anyway. Now away you all go. One, two, thrrreeeee!"

Away they went.

Gilbert hurried to the cupboard where he remembered father kept the little black box with some precious

papers inside. But when he found it, it was locked, so he went off on another scent.

Wilfred hunted upstairs, crawling under all the beds, with baby at his heels, enjoying the fun immensely.

Bang! bang! bang! went the cupboard doors as one by one they were opened and closed.

Sylvia wandered about quietly with a thoughtful look on her face.

"Now, what can it be?" she said to herself. "The most valuable thing in the house? Um. It can't be money, for there isn't much of that. And it can't be jewelry, for Mother hasn't any. Um. It might be a picture, but it isn't more than a foot square, and we haven't any pictures that size. Um. It might be one of those queer curios on the mantelpiece in the parlor, but hardly so, for it is something that can be opened. Yes, opened. What things can be opened? Boxes and bags and brief cases, and, um, yes, books!"

Why, there was an idea. Why hadn't she thought of that before? It might be one of the old books in the bookcase. She hurried over to it.

"Three more minutes!" called Mother from the kitchen.

"I've got something," cried Gilbert.

"So have I," shouted Wilfred, his voice seeming to come from the attic.

"And so have I," echoed baby from the same quarter.

Feverishly Sylvia looked along the rows of books, but which one to choose she could not tell. Many of the titles she did not even recognize. There were books on history, astronomy, literature, and all sorts of things, with here and there a big fat commentary and concordance. Suddenly, just between two of these large volumes she spied a smaller one, and a happy smile spread across her face.

"Got it!" she said to herself, as she picked it out and hurried with it to the dining room.

"Time!" called Mother.

Down came the others helter-skelter.

"Well, what have you found for me?" asked Mother.

"Your purse," said Gilbert.

"Ha, ha, ha!" laughed Mother. "So

you think that's the most valuable thing in this house!
Well, it isn't, by a long, long way, especially at the
end of the week."

"I think I've got it," said Wilfred, bringing forth a
dusty, old-fashioned mother-of-pearl workbox he had
found in the attic.

"Well, I never did!" exclaimed Mother. "How did
you find that? I haven't seen it for years and years. It
belonged to my grandmother, and it is very precious to
me; yet it isn't the most valuable thing that I hid spe-
cially and wanted you to find."

Wilfred looked rather disappointed.

"And what did you bring, baby dear?" asked
Mother.

"Just me," said baby, at which, of course, Mother
had to pick him up and hug him for a full minute.

"You surely are the sweetest thing," she said, kissing him. "But has nobody found what I hid?"

Sylvia was blushing a little, for she felt sure she had discovered the treasure, and at this moment produced her find.

"Well done!" cried Mother. "Sylvia has won! What made you think of it?"

"I don't know," said Sylvia. "I just saw it and guessed."

"Who'd have thought of that!" exclaimed Gilbert. "A Bible!"

"Yes," said Mother. "And I wonder you didn't all think of it together. Of course it's the most valuable thing in this house. When you open it you find it is full of the richest treasure. It is a gold mine of truth, full of beautiful stories of Jesus and His love. There is wonderful counsel here to keep us from making mistakes, from doing things we might be sorry for, and to tell us how to share at last in all the riches and glory of God's eternal kingdom. Why, there's nothing anywhere so precious as this."

"But you can buy it for half a dollar," said Gilbert.

"I know," said Mother. "But remember, when one of the early copies of the Book was found, not very long ago, it took five hundred thousand dollars to buy it. Why, Gilbert, there isn't another book in the world for which people would give five hundred thousand dol-

lars. The nearest to that was seventy-seven thousand dollars, paid for the original manuscript of *Alice in Wonderland*. Nobody would give *five hundred* thousand dollars for that or any other book. Only the Bible could bring such a price. Truly, the art of printing has made it cheap for us to buy, but it is just as precious inside as it ever was."

"Wish I'd thought of that," said Wilfred, looking woefully at the supper table.

"Never mind," said Sylvia gracefully, "I'll cut that best cake into five pieces and share it with everybody."

# Our Wonderful World

*J*N OLDEN DAYS IT used to be said that there were just seven "wonders of the world," and they included such things as the pyramids of Egypt, the hanging gardens of Babylon, and some of the other great works of man that have long since been forgotten by everybody.

What are the seven wonders of the world today? What would you say? Why not take time one day to make a list of all the wonderful things you have seen, or heard about, and then try to pick out the seven greatest of them all.

I suppose you would start off with radio, or possibly television, which is akin to it. That is truly a most marvelous invention, bordering on the miraculous, and still far beyond the understanding of most of us. Indeed, if the ancients could have seen a picture being sent hundreds of miles through the ether without any visible means of communication, they would either have cried out, "Witchcraft!" or have fallen down in worship before the instrument.

Early on your list you would, of course, have airplanes, helicopters, rocket ships, and the great Hughes flying boat with room for 700 passengers.

Yes, and just think of that young woman who, living in England, decided she would like to go back to her home in New Zealand, and flew all the way by herself in a few days. That was surely one of the most wonderful achievements of the century.

Then we might think of the mighty bridges that men have thrown across great chasms and rivers, gigantic structures that almost take your breath away as you look up at them, such as those stupendous structures over the Golden Gate and San Francisco Bay in California, or the Forth Bridge in Scotland, or the Sydney Bridge, in Australia.

There are the great tunnels also, miles long, blasted through the solid rock of the Alps. Why, I passed through the Simplon Tunnel some years ago, and it took nearly fifteen minutes to do so. I timed it.

What would not the Caesars have paid for a tunnel through the Alps! Certainly they would never have believed it possible that one could be made. They built some won-

derful roads in their day, too, but what would they
have thought of the beautiful Columbia River Highway or the two hundred-mile Pennsylvania Turnpike
with not a single crossroad on it?

Then there are all the great ships that plow the
oceans, each one containing a thousand marvels that
would have made the men of olden days gasp with
astonishment. Imagine Mark Anthony, or the famous
Cleopatra, being taken for a walk through the docks of
New York Harbor, and staring up open-mouthed at
the colossal proportions of the *Queen Mary,* the *Queen
Elizabeth,* perhaps the *America,* and half a dozen other
similar leviathans of the deep. Do you think you could
ever make them realize that these mountains of steel
could be driven through the water five times faster than
a Roman galley at full speed?

Should you go to a naval dockyard, you might see
the great battleships *North Carolina* or *New Mexico,*

giant floating fortresses crammed with the most marvelous inventions. Near them you would see submarines to add to your list—strange steel craft that can go to the bottom of the ocean and rise to the surface again at the will of their commanders.

Yet we have only begun. A walk around any large department store, yes, even Woolworth's, will give you a hundred suggestions of new wonders to record. Think of the beautiful fabrics that are produced so cheaply today, and of the intricate machines that make them.

There is the modern newspaper, too, not much to be admired for its contents, perhaps, but when you think of its origin in the great forests, and of all the work that goes into the making of it, surely it is one of the greatest marvels of the age.

And now comes the wonderful Palomar telescope in California, which enables astronomers to see perhaps twice as far as they ever saw before.

Having listed all these inventions of man, and many others besides, the record will still be by no means complete.

There are, in addition, all the great natural wonders we have not put down. Perhaps you have seen the Giants' Causeway on the north coast of Ireland. You could include that, for it is a very remarkable sight.

In many places in our wonderful world there are scenes of nature that are staggering in their immensity and beauty. Snow-capped peaks like the Himalayas, towering waterfalls hundreds of feet in height, like the Victoria Falls in Central Africa and, of course, Niagara Falls on the United States-Canadian border.

North America possesses an unusual number of natural wonders, such as the Grand Canyon of the Colorado, a vast chasm, hundreds of feet deep, and many miles in length, washed out by water action long centuries ago. It has also the famous Carlsbad Caverns, the largest in the world, where, far beneath the surface of the earth, innumerable rock formations, some of them of enormous size, blend in pictures of majestic and enchanting beauty.

Marvelous as are the works of man, I somehow feel that these wonders that have come from the hand of God are still more impressive.

Think of the gigantic sequoia trees of California. Forests of these massive trees are still to be found there. Some of the largest are more than three hundred feet high and have a diameter, at their base, of thirty feet and more. If you will look at the picture

illustrating this story, you will realize how very big they are. Fancy being able to drive a car right through the trunk of a tree!

These trees are the oldest living things on the earth. Scores of them are over one thousand years old, some are two thousand, and a few, it is said, are at least three thousand. If so, it means that when Jesus was born in Bethlehem, these hoary old giants had already been growing for a thousand years, and they have lived through all the history of the world since then. What stories they could tell if only they could speak!

They were alive in Solomon's day, and when great Pharaohs sat on the throne of Egypt. Babylon had not been thought of when their first shoots rose above the earth, and when Rome was but a village, their branches towered into the skies.

What man could make a living thing like this?

True, men made the pyramids, and they stand as they did many thousands of years ago, save where they have fallen into decay or been damaged by vandals; but the big trees have lived and gone on growing all this long, long time. That is the work of God.

And if we are looking for wonders, there are the stars above us, or the tiny blades of grass under our feet. There is the daily miracle of the tides, and of the sand on the seashore, which acts as a barrier that the sea may not pass over it. There is the miracle of the birds, how they sing so sweetly, how they fly so swiftly and so gracefully through the air. There are all the miracles of the little things, the beauty of the butterfly, the persistence of the ant, the thrift of the bee.

Why, we are surrounded with wonders we cannot begin to name or number, things more marvelous than anything that ever came forth from the mind of man.

Long, long ago that wise old patriarch Job came to the same conclusion, and he said, thinking of God, "Which doeth great things past finding out; yea, and wonders without number." Job 9:10.

Surely we may say with David, "O Lord, how manifold are Thy works! in wisdom hast Thou made them all: the earth is full of Thy riches." Ps. 104:24.

# Cutting the Wrong Grass

*L*ITTLE JAMES IS ONE of the dearest little baby boys you ever saw. If you could see him, I am sure you would want to pick him up in your arms and hug him. But, well, he is a real boy, even though he is so young, and just as full of mischief as boys usually are.

You'll never guess what he did the other day. Every time I think about it I laugh all over—though I suppose I should cry because of what nearly happened.

Well, it was this way: Master James was in his garden with his Daddy. I chanced to be quite near, and so saw everything.

His Daddy was cutting the grass with a lawn mower. On the lawn was a pair of shears.

Baby James, anxious to help his Daddy, picked up the shears and started cutting the grass.

143

"Look, Daddy," he cried, "I'm helping you cut the grass."

Daddy looked and smiled his thanks, but told him he should not play with the sharp shears.

Just then Prince ran onto the lawn.

Prince is their dog, you know, a little dog with lots of hair—the kind of dog that really would look nicer if he could go to the barber and have a bob or a shingle.

At any rate, little James seemed to think so, for, leaving his grass cutting, he gave chase to Prince, shears in hand.

Unfortunately, he missed Prince's hair and caught his hind leg, and what might have happened if little James's arms had been stronger I don't like to suggest.

But the sight of that poor little dog parading across the lawn with the shears attached to his hind leg, and with the astonished little James looking on, is one that I shall not soon forget!

Of course, James's Daddy saw it, too, which was rather unfortunate for James. What happened next it wouldn't be fair to tell you, but I rather think James will try to remember in the future that it is always best to do what Daddy says, and to do it at once.

Oh, by the way, I should add that Prince still has four legs.

To K. MARTIN

**One Day Jackie Had Brought a Beautiful New Yacht to Sail in the Pond. Dickie Wanted to Play With It Too, but Jackie Selfishly Said No**

# Jackie's Mended Yacht

*J*ACKIE WAS FEELING
so miserable he almost wished he could die. Even the
presence of Chummie didn't make him feel much better, comforting though he was.

You see, there was a nice big pond in Jackie's garden, with lots of water for floating boats, and Jackie and
Dickie—the little boy next door—had had the most
wonderful time together there.

Then one day Jackie had brought out a beautiful
new yacht that his Father had given him, and, of
course, Dickie had wanted to play with it, too. Jackie
had selfishly said no; so pretty soon there had been a
quarrel. Then they had started to fight over the yacht,
and while they were carrying on like this, they had both
got too near the edge of the pond, and, before they
could save themselves, had fallen with a great splash
into the water!

What a sight they had both looked when at last
they had managed to crawl out, drenched to the skin,
and covered with slimy mud!

Unfortunately, it had been rather chilly the day they fell in, so both boys had caught bad colds and had to stay in bed for several days.

This was why Jackie was feeling so miserable.

His beautiful new yacht was smashed. He had quarreled with his best friend, Dickie. He had a bad cold and cough, and Mamma had said that he could not go outdoors again for at least another week. Worse still, he had had to have the doctor come to see him every day, and he just hated having the doctor take his temperature, look down his throat, and thump his chest all over, just as though it were a drum!

"Oh, dear me!" he sighed, "shall I ever be better? Shall I ever be able to go out and play in the garden again? How I wish I hadn't quarreled with Dickie over that yacht! Why didn't I let him have just one turn with it? Now I suppose Dickie won't ever come over here again."

Just as he was thinking like this and feeling very, very sorry for himself, he thought he heard someone whispering his name.

"Jackie! Ssh!"

He pulled back a curtain and looked out.

Down below, under the window, was Dickie. So Dickie had got better first, and had come back to see him after all.

"Open the window," whispered Dickie. "Quietly, so nobody will hear us. I'm not supposed to be over here yet, but I just had to come."

Jackie looked around to make sure that nobody was about, and cautiously opened the window.

"Throw me a bit of

string," said Dickie. "I've got something for you."

"Haven't got any string up here," said Jackie.

"Aw, look for a bit," said Dickie. "There may be something about that will do instead."

Jackie looked, and all he could find was a roll of tape in one of Mamma's dressing-table drawers.

"Will this do?" he whispered.

"Fine!" whispered Dickie. "Hold on to one end and drop the other down to me."

Jackie dropped the tape out the window, wondering whatever it could be that Dickie wanted to send up to him.

There was a pause while Dickie tied something on the end.

"Pull away," he said presently. "And I hope everything's all right again now." Then he ran away as silently as he had come.

Jackie pulled at the tape, and to his amazement up came his lovely yacht, just as perfect as the day he first took it to the pond, with the mast mended, and all the sails and strings in place again.

What joy! And to think that Dickie had done it, that Dickie wasn't angry with him any more.

He was just bringing the yacht in through the window when he heard a noise behind him.

"Jackie!" cried Mamma. "Whatever are you doing by that open window? You'll catch your death of cold.

Haven't you been ill enough already without——"

Then she noticed the yacht.

"How did you get that?" she asked, all surprised.

"Dickie brought it," cried Jackie with delight. "Dickie did! He must have forgiven me for being so cross with him. Now we can play again, can't we?"

And Jackie looked so happy, so very much better all of a sudden, that Mamma forgot all about the open window and her precious ball of tape that she had just spied draped over the window sill.

"I hope that after all this," she said, "you will never quarrel with anybody any more."

"I won't. Surely I won't," said Jackie eagerly, and Chummie wagged his tail so hard that he must have been trying to say, "Amen."

# Paul's Lesson

*P*AUL'S GREAT AMBI-
tion in life at the moment was to make a sailing boat.
He had found a piece of wood about two feet long and
six inches square, and was proceeding to hollow it out
with a mallet and a chisel.

If you have never done this, you have missed one of
the joys of life. At any rate, Paul enjoyed it. He became
so interested that he could think of nothing else. As
soon as he returned from school every evening, he
would rush off to his little workshop and start on his
job again.

Gradually the piece of wood took shape. Little by
little, chip by chip, the hole became deeper and deeper.
There was not much left to do now, and soon he could
nail on the deck and put up the mast and sails.

Then came the Sabbath. From his earliest years
Paul had learned that this was a day to be kept holy.
He had been to church on this day as far back as he
could remember. Ordinary work was always laid aside.
He kept his very best books to read on this day. To all
the family it was a time of rest and peace.

This week, however, the Sabbath seemed to Paul to have come at the wrong time. More than anything else he wanted to finish his boat. There were only a few days left before the holidays, and he feared that he would not have it ready in time. If only he could work just a little while longer, he would be able to finish hollowing out the hull at least.

In the morning he went to church as usual. In the afternoon, however, he told Mother that he would rather not go out for a walk with her. He would look after the house while Mother went out, he said.

Mother had not been gone long, however, before Paul closed the book he was reading and got up off his chair. He knew that he had not really read a line of the book. All the time he had been thinking about

the boat. Something seemed to be shouting in his ears, "Boat, boat, boat!"

He wandered about the house for a little while, still uncertain what to do. Very faintly another voice said to him, "Remember the Sabbath day, to keep it holy."

Then the first voice started again, "Boat, boat, boat!"

Gradually Paul moved toward his workshop. He opened the door and looked in. There could be no harm in looking in, of course, even on the Sabbath day, he told himself.

Yes, there was the boat, just as he had left it the evening before, almost finished. Another half hour's work, thought Paul, and the hull would be ready for the deck. What a pity to have to wait another whole day before he could touch it!

He went in, shut the door behind him, and walked over to the boat. Admiringly he stroked his hand over the smooth surface of the wood.

Then, before he quite realized what he was doing, he had picked up the mallet and given one bang to the chisel. The noise resounded through the stillness of the house and made Paul just a little frightened. He looked around to make sure the door was shut.

Bang! He gave the chisel another hit.

Again he felt afraid. Would Mother hear? What would she think of him? But there, Mother was bound to be out for another half hour. She always did go out for at least an hour's walk on Sabbath afternoons.

Bang! Out flew another chip of wood.

Paul became bolder. Every hit was a little harder. But he was still very nervous.

"Oh!" he cried all of a sudden. The mallet had missed the top of the chisel and had come down on his thumbnail.

Tears filled his eyes, and he danced around the room for a minute until the pain had eased. He began to wonder whether he should have stayed, but now there was only such a little bit left to do he thought he might as well finish it.

Bang! Bang! Bang!

"Oh!" cried Paul in dismay. This time he had hit the chisel a little too hard, and it had gone right through the boat. His beautiful work was spoiled. He could have wept, for now it would be difficult to make the boat watertight.

He was almost persuaded to stop, but the misfortune had made him desperate.

Bang! Bang! Bang! He hammered away faster than ever, very fearful now that Mother might return any minute and find him there.

"Oh!"

The chisel had slipped and cut his hand. It was a bad cut, and Paul knew it. He wrapped his handkerchief around it and ran from the room.

"Mother, Mother!" he cried, "I've cut myself badly. Mother, where are you?"

Fortunately, Mother was nearing home. She heard Paul's cries some distance away, and came running to him as fast as she could.

As Mother entered the front door, Paul fell over in a faint, and it was some time before he was well enough to explain what had happened.

When he opened his eyes again he found himself sitting in one of the armchairs in the dining room. Mother was bathing his forehead with cold water.

Paul began to stare at something on the wall.

"What's the matter, dearie?" said Mother soothingly. "Don't look so worried."

"Look," said Paul, "to think of that being in front of me now."

"What?" asked Mother, very much puzzled.

"That!" said Paul.

Mother looked and at last began to understand. For there she read the old familiar words:

"A Sabbath well spent
Brings a week of content
And strength for the tasks of the morrow;
But a Sabbath profaned,
Whate'er may be gained,
Is a certain forerunner of sorrow."

**Mamma Hurried to the Door, Rather Hot and Bothered. She Opened the Door Sharply—and There Stood Grandma With Her Handbags and Trunk**

# How Grandma Came for Christmas

*A*T LAST THE DAY HAD come to open the money boxes! How long it had taken to fill them! What hard work it had meant, what careful saving, what giving up of candy and nice ribbons and special treats! To Hilda and Mona it had seemed as if they would never be allowed to open them, and sometimes they had even said it wasn't worth while putting the money in.

But at last the day had come! It was a week before Christmas, and of course everybody was wanting all the money he could find for presents and new dresses and things. How glad the children were that they had heeded their Mother, and kept the boxes unopened till now! Mother was right, after all.

Click! went the key in Mona's little cash box, and there inside she saw the piles of pennies, with nickels, dimes, quarters, and one whole half dollar. What joy! She counted it all up, and Hilda counted it afterward, just to make sure it was right. Fancy! Two dollars and

fifty-one cents! What a lot of money for a little girl
to have!

"Now you open yours," said Mona. "I wonder who
has the most?"

Hilda's was a strange-looking money box, but it certainly held money tightly. It was such a job to get it out.
She had to use a knife, but as she poked it in, out came
the pennies, nickels, dimes, quarters, and two half dollars. It was a lovely sight.

"Oh!" said Mona, "you have more than I!"

"It looks like it," said Hilda. "Let's count it up.
One, two, three. Why,
I believe there's more
than three dollars!"

And so there was. It
came to $3.28. How
happy they both were!
Never before had they
had so much money to
spend all at once.

Then came the big
question. What should
they spend it on? Soon
they realized how little
they had really saved.
There were so many
things to buy, and most

of them cost more than they had both saved together.

Mona thought she would like to get a very pretty party frock, but how far would $2.51 go? Hilda's first thought was for a beautiful handbag, the kind with two pockets in the middle and a mirror. But again, how far would $3.28 go? Then they talked of other things they would like—so many things—but try as they would they could not stretch their money nearly far enough to cover all their desires.

"I'm getting tired of trying to decide," said Hilda. "This money is a bother."

"Do you know," said Mona, "I wonder if the trouble is that we are just trying to spend it all on ourselves?"

Hilda sat very quiet and still. "Perhaps it is," she said after a while.

"Just for fun," said Mona, "let's try to think how we could spend it on some other people."

"Mamma, for instance," said Hilda.

"Yes, or even grandma," said Mona.

"All right. You write down what you would buy for them, and I'll do the same."

So they both found pencil and paper and started to write. Hilda soon made a long list—long enough to use up her $3.28 many times over.

"You don't seem to have put down much, Mona," she said, looking at her paper.

4-11

"No," said Mona, "but I've got an idea. I've thought of something that would be a beautiful present for both Mamma and grandma."

"Come on, then, let's have it," said Hilda.

"Well," said Mona, "you know how Mamma has been longing to have grandma come down here to stay with her for a while? Well, the only reason she doesn't come is that she can't afford the fare and Mamma can't afford to send it to her. Wouldn't it be just wonderful if we were to send grandma her fare ourselves, and invite her down to surprise Mamma?"

"Mona, you are a genius!" said Hilda. "I should enjoy that much more than a new handbag. Let's do it right now."

"Isn't it just lovely?" said Mona. "I'm so glad you like the idea. I'd much rather see Mamma happy than

162

have a new dress. Let's get a pen and some writing paper. You'll write the letter, won't you?"

"All right," said Hilda. "You tell me what to say."

So together they wrote to their grandma:

"Our dear Grandma,

"We all want you very much to come down here for Christmas. Mona and I have been saving up for a long time to pay your fare, and you will find it in this letter. Don't lose it, and be sure to come soon. We shall expect you next week.

"With lots of love from
"Hilda and Mona."

"O Mona," said Hilda when she had finished writing; "whatever will Mamma say when grandma comes?"

"Oh, that's part of the fun. She'll just be so pleased and surprised she won't know what to do with herself."

Picking up their money and putting on their coats, the two went down to the post office, bought a postal money order for $5, and mailed it off to grandma. Chuckling all over and enjoying their secret immensely, they returned home to await events.

For the next few days the girls could not settle to anything. Every footstep made them jump, and every creak of the front gate gave them a start. They felt inside themselves that they had done something big and beautiful, not unmixed with mischief, and they just couldn't keep still. Every now and then they would burst out laughing, for no apparent reason whatever. Mamma wondered what could have gone wrong with them.

Then at last came a different knock at the door.

"Hilda, there's someone at the door," called Mamma. "Go and see who it is."

But Hilda guessed that the great moment had come, and she wanted Mamma to have the surprise they had planned so long. "I really can't go," she said. "Do please go yourself, Mamma."

So Mamma hurried to the door, rather hot and bothered, thinking it was the baker or the milkman. She opened the door sharply—and there stood grandma, with her handbags and trunk, as if she had come to stay a month.

"Well, well!" cried Mamma. "Whoever—whatever! Isn't this wonderful! But how did you come? Who could have dreamed you would be here for Christmas!"

"Why, didn't you expect me?" said grandma, equally surprised.

There was a loud chuckle in the background.

"Ah, those two young scamps," said grandma. "I guess they are at the bottom of this."

And then came the explanations, and everybody was very happy. After the excitement had died down, grandma called the children to her and, slowly and mysteriously, opened her trunk.

"I'm not too old to use my fingers yet," she said, pulling out a couple of parcels. "Here's a little dress I've been working for Mona, and I've got a wee handbag made all of beads for Hilda."

"Never!" cried the girls together, looking at each other in amazement.

"Why, don't you want them?" asked grandma.

"Want them! I should say we do! They are just perfect," said Hilda. "But how did you know? They are the very things we were going to buy for ourselves with the money we had saved in our boxes."

"Well, did you ever!" exclaimed grandma. "Do you know, girls," she said, "I believe the good old Book is right when it says, 'He that hath pity upon the poor lendeth unto the Lord; and that which he hath given will He pay him again.'"

# "Daredevils"

*D*O YOU KNOW WHAT I can do now?" cried Maurice, running indoors excitedly.

"I can't guess," said Mother, "but you are always up to something."

"Well, at last I can ride my bicycle without putting my hands on the handle bars."

"That may be very clever," said Mother, "but I'm afraid it's not very sensible."

"Why not?" asked Maurice, rather crestfallen. "All the boys try to do it, and I can do it now better than any of them."

"Maybe you can," said Mother, "but what is the purpose of it?"

"Aw, I don't know," said Maurice; "it's lots of fun."

"I suppose it must be," said Mother, "but isn't it rather risky?"

"Risky? Oh, you're always talking about things being risky," said Maurice, rather annoyed.

"Of course, we all have to take risks sometimes," said Mother, "but why take unnecessary risks?"

"There's no risk in that," said Maurice. "It's easy."

"Well, I don't like your doing it," said Mother, "especially with so much traffic on the roads today. After all, what are handle bars for, if not to be used to steady yourself?"

"Oh, dear!" exclaimed Maurice, "don't worry so, Mother; it's quite all right."

With this he bounded out of the house, closing the door, I am sorry to say, with a much louder bang than usual.

A moment later he was on his bicycle again, gliding down the hill from his home, his arms folded in front of him and his face indicating supreme indifference to all his Mother's caution.

Gathering speed, he glided along in great style, glancing from side to side to see whether anyone might be looking at him.

Near the bottom of the hill he spied two little girls standing at the roadside, and consequently sat up a little straighter, folded his arms a little more confidently, and tilted his chin just a little bit higher. He was not "showing off," of course, oh, dear, no! Just letting the little girls see how fast a boy could ride down a hill without holding the handle bars; that's all.

What Maurice failed to see, however, was a brick lying in the road, right in the path of his bicycle. If his chin had not been tilted so high, if he had not been sitting up so very straight, if he had not had his arms folded, he would have seen it easily, and everything would have been different; but there, he didn't see it, and a moment later he felt a terrific bump. The front wheel twisted, the handle bars swung right around, and before Maurice had time to think what was happening, he had crashed into the ditch at the side of the road.

Some men working near, hearing the noise, ran to see what had happened, and found Maurice floundering in mud, with his bicycle, all bent and broken, on top of him.

What a pickle he was in! Slimy water dripped from his clothes as they dragged him out, while his face, hands, and knees were red with blood from cuts and scratches.

The men were very kind, and helped Maurice up the hill again to his home, one of them carrying the wrecked machine over his shoulder.

"Oh, dear!" cried Mother, her eyes wide with alarm, as she opened the door and looked out on the strange procession. "Whatever has happened?"

Yet she hardly needed to ask. She guessed. It was, in fact, just what she had been expecting for some time.

"My poor boy!" she said, leading Maurice indoors and starting to clean him up. "What a mercy you weren't killed."

She changed his clothes and washed his wounds, binding them up till he looked as if he had just come back from a war.

Then with Maurice at last comfortably—that is, more or less comfortably—seated by the fire, she reminded him of the conversation they had had less than an hour before.

"It is right to take risks in a good cause," she added, "or to help people in distress, but to take risks just to gratify our vanity is foolishness. There are always people—provided others are looking on—who are ready to go and peer over the edge of a precipice; or stand on the end of a pier when the waves are dashing over and the wind is blowing hard; or drive their cars at breakneck speed; or swim in the sea beyond their depth; but these are not the truly brave people. Such actions are a form of pride, not of courage; an effort to call attention to  oneself, and so are really just cheap, tawdry self-advertisement."

"But what has that to do with me and my accident?" asked Maurice.

"Everything," said Mother. "For the moment you were just the same as these I have mentioned, a daredevil like the rest, and the disaster that usually comes sooner or later to all daredevils came to you."

"Um," said Maurice, reflecting. "All the same it's rather nice to ride a bike without having your hands on the handle bars."

"Maybe it is," said Mother, "but I don't really think it's worth while, do you?"

Maurice mournfully surveyed his bandages.

"I don't believe it is, after all," he said.

170

# Under the Falls

*H*AVE YOU EVER BEEN to Niagara Falls? If not, I'm sure you would like to go someday, wouldn't you?

They are one of the great natural wonders of the world, and no one can look at that mighty mass of water dashing helter-skelter toward the precipice, then suddenly falling through rising mists of spray upon the rocks beneath, without feeling thrilled at the grandeur of it all.

Yet most people who visit this wonderful scene never see it in the fullness of its majesty and power. To do this, you must needs go down underneath the falls, and let the water come right over you.

Underneath?

Yes, indeed, for somebody has cut a tunnel through the solid rock, so that visitors, after going down an elevator, can walk beneath the roaring torrent and feel the spray dash over them.

Rather a wet job, eh?

I should say so, and, of course, you have to dress for the occasion. But you can hire the things you need right

171

on the spot, and oh, how funny they make you look! In the picture on page 174 you can see some people in these waterproof clothes. They almost look like gnomes out of some fairy story, don't they?

Well, it seems like a sort of fairyland, it is all so strange and wonderful.

Come along with me, and look up at this marvelous sight.

Isn't it just tremendous? There seems no end to the mighty flood as it

172

comes roaring down all about you, wetting you from head to foot. Water—oceans and oceans of it—whipped to sparkling whiteness in its downward sweep, seems to come tumbling upon you, crashing, dashing, splashing as it sweeps magnificently on toward the sea.

Looking far up through the glorious falls, we catch a glimpse of the sky, and suddenly the love of Jesus becomes more real. Why, of course, His love is just like this, poured out from heaven in a mighty, ceaseless, overwhelming torrent that surrounds and envelops us.

The Bible tells us that there is no limit to His love, for He saves "to the uttermost." Hebrews 7:25.

And it never ceases, for He loves us "unto the end." John 13:1.

Neither is there any measure to His love, for "as the heaven is high above the earth, so great is His mercy toward them that fear Him." Psalms 103:11.

Like mighty Niagara, it flows all around us, comforting us, inspiring us, and supplying all our needs, "according to His riches in glory." Philippians 4:19.

It makes me think of a beautiful hymn we often sing:

> "O the deep, deep love of Jesus,
>    Vast, unmeasured, boundless, free;
>   Rolling as a mighty ocean
>    In its fullness over me.

Have you found His love to be like that—like an ocean of goodness and friendliness and graciousness rolling right over you?

You may, if you wish.

Just stand under the falls and look up.

# Cupboard Love

*H*AVE YOU EVER
bought a bag of candy and then found your little
brother or your little sister coming to you and saying, so
earnestly and tenderly, "I do love you so"?

That's cupboard love.

Or maybe at school sometime, when you have
been peeling a big apple, someone has sat down beside
you and said, "I like being in your class," or, "It's nice
to have you around."

That's cupboard love, too.

Cupboard love is not true love. In fact, it isn't really
love at all. It's a sort of selfishness, and rather deceitful,
too. It is interested in things, not people. It wants the
gift, but not the giver.

Jimmy had a very bad case of cupboard love. When
his uncle would come to see him, he would pretend so
hard to be fond of him that uncle would take him to
town and buy him some new toy. Then when uncle
had gone away again, Jimmy would be heard to re-
mark, "He's a funny old man, isn't he?"

He tried it on Mamma, too. Whenever she would

come back from a shopping expedition with lots of parcels, Jimmy would at first be so loving and so polite, expecting that one of the parcels would be for him. But if he found there was nothing for him, he would pout and weep and carry on alarmingly.

Then one day Mamma became ill and had to go away to the hospital. She was so sorry to leave her home and Jimmy, and every day she looked forward to her return. While lying in bed she would picture the glad moment when at last she would be walking up the familiar garden path again and Jimmy would run out and throw his arms around her in wild, joyous welcome. She lived for that moment, and every passing hour the thought of it became more precious to her.

Then at last the doctor said she was well enough to go home again. How her heart beat fast with excitement! She was going back at last to see everybody and everything she loved so dearly —and especially Jimmy.

The car pulled up at the house, and just as Mamma had expected, Jimmy ran out to meet her, eyes ablaze, arms outstretched. But as he ran down the path to meet her, his first words made her heart sad. She was so disappointed.

"What do you have for me?" he asked. "Did you bring me a parcel?"

"So that's all he wants," thought Mamma. "Not me, but an old brown-paper parcel!"

She walked right by him and into the house.

"But I want to love you," cried Jimmy, running after her and sensing that something was wrong.

"Go and get some brown paper and string," said Mamma very coldly. "Tie it up and love that."

And Mamma left Jimmy to his thoughts.

Hard as it seemed, it worked. Jimmy understood perfectly. When bedtime came, he went over to where Mamma was sitting and whispered, "I really do love you more than parcels. I'm really glad you came home."

Mamma took him into her arms, for here was the true love for which her heart had been aching so long.

4-12

# Broken Crackers

*H*ERE IS ONE OF THE
sweetest little stories I have ever heard.

How I wish I knew the little boy's name! But I
don't; so I shall just have to call him Tommy. The
angels will understand.

Now, Tommy was a very poor little boy whose
Father was out of work and whose Mother took in the
neighbors' washing to earn a few nickels. They lived all
together in one room, with Tommy's brothers and
sisters, in one of the dreadful slum districts of London.
Yet terrible as were the conditions under which little
Tommy lived, he had a heart of gold.

One Sunday afternoon, while he was playing in the
gloomy, narrow street near his home, he noticed an
unusual number of people going by dressed in their
best clothes.

His curiosity was aroused.

"Where are they all going?" he asked his boy
friends.

"Church, I suppose," said one. "Goin' to sing
'ymns and listen to a man preach."

"Shucks!" said another. "Not all them lot. They're goin' to the 'arvest festival."

"The what?" asked Tommy.

" 'Arvest festival, I said. Don't yer know what that is? Where they 'ave potatoes and carrots and turnips and cabbages all around the pulpit. 'Aven't yer seen one of 'em?"

Tommy confessed that he hadn't.

"Then yer'd better go along and see this one," said his friend.

Tommy thought it was a good idea, and ran off toward the place of meeting.

It wasn't a church after all, only a mission hall. He recognized it at once. "Hoxton Market Mission," said the big notice over the door. Of course, he had been there several times for meals

when he was very hungry. He remembered singing there with a lot of other children and hearing a kind gentleman tell about the love of Jesus.

Mingling with the people who were entering the building, he managed at last to put his head round the front door and peep in.

What a surprise! He had never seen anything like this before. His little friend was right. There were potatoes and carrots and turnips and cabbages all around the pulpit. And lots of other things, too—apples and oranges and bananas and great big bunches of grapes and loaves of bread bigger than any he had ever seen in his life before.

"Phew!" he whistled softly in sheer astonishment, while his sparkling eyes and wide-open mouth told how surprised he was.

"You seem very interested in everything, my little man," said a kindly voice.

Tommy looked up fearfully, and started to run away out of the building.

"Don't go away. You can stay if you wish."

"Can I?" asked Tommy. "But what's it all for?"

"Don't you know? Why, once a year everybody brings something that has been grown in the earth to show that they remember that all good things come from God and that they are thankful for the harvest."

"Do they have to grow them themselves?"

"Oh, no. They couldn't do that here, where there aren't any gardens or fields for miles and miles. They save up their pennies, and buy something, and then afterward all the things are given away to people who are very, very poor."

"Does everybody have to bring something?" asked Tommy wistfully.

"Oh, no," said the kind lady. "Only those who feel able to. Some haven't any pennies at all, and Jesus understands all about that."

"Um," said Tommy, thinking. "I think I won't stay now."

So saying, he turned and slipped away quickly through the stream of people still coming to the mission.

He was feeling in his pocket now. Yes, there it was,

his one and only penny. He had picked it up in the gutter only yesterday, and was keeping it safely hidden away for some special treat.

"Perhaps they will have something in the candy store," he said to himself. "I hope it won't be too small. Those loaves of bread are so very large."

He entered the store and looked around. Lollypops? No, they wouldn't do, not for an occasion like this. Marshmallows? No. You wouldn't get enough for a penny.

Ah, what was that over there?

"Broken Crackers—Penny a Bag."

Crackers? Yes, they would do. They were just as much "grown in the earth" as the big loaves of bread. And this bag looked fine and big, too.

Tommy bought a bag and hastened out of the shop toward the mission.

He hadn't the courage to go in the front door, but he knew there was a back way in, and if it should be open——

It was.

He felt very nervous, fearing someone would notice him. But there were still people going in, and some through the back door, too. So he went in with them, yes, right past all the beautiful things piled up round the pulpit.

Tightly in his hot, grubby little hand he held the precious bag.

"Quick!" he thought to himself, "before anybody sees."

Right beside the great big loaf he dropped the precious bag.

Nobody saw him do it, for there were many people passing, and those already in their seats were too busy talking to each other.

Tommy glided to a seat as far out of sight as possible, and not a soul, not even the kind lady who had spoken to him, knew he was there.

The meeting over, he made his way back to his gloomy home, feeling an unusual happiness in his brave little heart.

Heaven was happier, too, I believe, as the angels brought back news of his lovely deed.

The bag of broken crackers was found, of course.

Somebody discovered it there afterward, under the great big loaf, and dropped a tear as he thought of the precious, childish love that had inspired the gift.

He told me that he thought this was the richest gift of all.

I think it was, too, don't you?

And it made me think of a story Jesus once told about a poor widow who went to the temple one day and saw the people giving their offerings, and "she threw in two mites, which make a farthing."

And Jesus said to His disciples: "Verily I say unto you, That this poor widow hath cast more in, than all they which have cast into the treasury: for all they did cast in of their abundance; but she of her want did cast in all that she had." Mark 12:43, 44.

184

# Where Angels Weep

*T*HINKING OF TOMMY has reminded me of another story I have wanted to tell you for a long time.

It's about Tommy's home; or rather about the homes of hundreds of other poor little boys and girls who live in the slums of the great cities of the world.

I have been in many of them, and would like to take you along with me on a visit if you'll come. For if somebody didn't take you, I'm sure you'd never go.

If you were to go to London, you would visit the Tower and Westminster Abbey and St. Paul's. In Paris you would go to the Eiffel Tower and the Louvre and Napoleon's Tomb. In New York you would go up the Empire State Building and visit Radio City and places like that. But you would never think of going round the corner, off the bright main streets where the fine buildings and the nice stores are, to see how the poor people live.

Sometimes, though, we should go round that corner, just so we might understand something of their

need, and try to think how we may help them best, yes, and be more thankful for the rich blessings God has given to us.

But see, here we are, in the very street where Tommy lives. It is very dismal, for there are no nice lawns and gardens in front of the houses. Instead, they are all joined together in long, long rows on both sides of the street. The front doors are close together and open right onto the pavement. There are many, many children playing about, some in the gutters, and all very dirty and poorly dressed.

Over there is a house with the blinds pulled down. Evidently there is something the matter there. Let's go and see what it is.

Several families live in this house, each family having one room. Yes, one room for Father, Mother, and all the children. How would you like to live like that?

We knock on the door. It is opened by a very sad-looking man. He has tears in his eyes, for he has been weeping.

He takes us into a little back room. It is only nine feet square. Measure that out sometime, and see how very small it is. He tells us that in this room he and his wife and three children have lived, but they are not there now. His wife has just died, also one of his children. They didn't have enough to eat; so when sickness came, they were not strong enough to resist it.

There is no furniture in this room, only a coffin, with the poor children's Mamma inside.

Where are the children?

We find the two of them in the next room, asleep in the neighbor's bed. Poor little motherless things!

But look at that cat by the cupboard! How alert it is! Its whiskers are sticking straight out. And no wonder; it is waiting for the rats that come up from the sewer every night.

Ugh! I can hear you say. Sewer rats in the bedroom! Yes, but wait, there's more to show you yet.

Here is another house in the next street. It is a little larger than the first one we saw, but twenty-five people live in it.

The family we want to see lives in the basement. There are just two rooms down there—a bedroom and a kitchen. Here live a Father, Mother, and five children.

Let's look in the bedroom.

There are holes all over the floor, some of them covered with pieces of metal cut from tins of various kinds. They are rat holes, and as fast as one hole is covered up, the rats make another.

And see those cracks around the fireplace? At night beetles come out of those cracks, hundreds of them, and crawl all over the room.

Dreadful! I know it is, but look, there's a big old-fashioned iron bedstead over there, with one of those uncomfortable springs that sag in the middle and throw everybody into the center.

But surely nobody sleeps in there!

Oh, yes. That's the children's bed. They all sleep in it—at least, four of them do—down in that dreadful dungeon among the rats and mice and beetles and many other living things, too. Poor things!

Now let's go——

But you don't want to see any more, I know. All right, then, just come with me to Tommy's mission—you know, the one where he saw the harvest festival. I want you to see how the dear people here care for the poor little ones who come to them out of these terrible homes.

Every afternoon seven hundred children are fed in this place. The hall will hold only five hundred; so the others wait their turn outside—sometimes in the rain!

Let's watch them awhile.

It is ten minutes to five, and the crowd of excited children are pouring in, dozens and dozens and dozens of them, all very dirty and very ragged, but, oh, so happy that in a few moments they are going to get something to eat.

Just look at them. You never saw such a sight in all your life. On the front row there isn't one with a whole pair of shoes. All of their toes are sticking through, and they have no stockings. Most of the clothes don't fit anyway, because they were bought long ago for somebody else.

Their hair is all tangled and matted, and their bright little faces are as soiled as can be. As for their noses—oh, dear, their noses!

Poor dears!

Now we can smell the food. It will soon be ready. The delicious aroma brings renewed eagerness into every face. They can hardly wait.

A whistle is blown, and a kind gentleman speaks.
"What shall we do before we eat?" he asks.
"Say grace!" cry several.
"Yes, of course," he says. "And what else?"
"Sing!" shout others.
"Good. Let's sing, and let Jesus know how much we love Him."

Sing! Can they sing? And at such a time?

Can they? I should say they can. I wish you could hear them sometime. Though it is a long time since I

last heard them, their happy songs still ring in my ears.
I wish I could hear them now.

And listen. What are they singing?

> "Wide, wide as the ocean,
>     High as the heavens above,
> Deep, deep as the deepest sea
>     Is my Saviour's love.
> I, though so unworthy,
>     Still am a child of His care;
> For His Word teaches me
> That His love reaches me
>     Everywhere."

How very beautiful! Think of their homes, their
dreadful, squalid homes, and yet they sing of the love
of Jesus reaching them there!

But listen again. They are singing another song
now, just as sweet as the other:

> "Over and over,
>     Like the mighty sea,
> Comes the love of Jesus,
>     Rolling over me!"

Over and over, round and round, faster and faster,
they move their dirty little hands as they come, again
and again, to that last wonderful line.

Look at them! Their pale, wan faces are wreathed

in smiles, their mouths wide open, as they sing their loudest, "Rolling over me!"

How can they do it? Doesn't it make you wish you were as grateful for the love of God as they are?

And now the food. At last! Are they glad to see it? I should say so. And no knives or forks or spoons to reduce speed as they get to work. All too soon it is gone, and they file slowly out so that the others who have been patiently waiting outside may come in.

Poor little children of the slums! Should we not say a prayer for them tonight?

192

# CHILDREN OF THE DARKNESS

Dear children of the darkness,
  We think of you tonight,
And pray the dear Lord Jesus
  To end your dreadful plight.

We sorrow at your suffering,
  We weep for all your pain,
And pray the dear Lord Jesus
  To smile on you again.

We know that in His mercy
  He seeth all you do,
And pray the dear Lord Jesus
  To make things up to you.

We wish that we could help you,
  And all we can we will;
But soon the dear Lord Jesus
  Will do it better still.

He comes again in glory
  To end all sin and woe,
That those who love Him truly
  Eternal joys may know.

Dear children of the darkness,
  Your night will soon be o'er,
And light and love and beauty
  Be yours forevermore!

UNCLE ARTHUR.

**It Is Fun to See the Bears Come Out of the Woods and Beg for Food. This Picture
Shows a Mother Bear and Her Two Cubs Asking for Something to Eat**

# A Bold, Bad Bear

*N*OT MANY WEEKS AGO I saw a most amusing sight in Yosemite—that famous beauty spot of California.

Personally, I didn't like the bears. Bears, to my mind, should be locked up, and not left roaming around public parks all on their own. It really isn't nice to meet a big fat bear on the public highway, or have one come scratching at the door of your tent if you decide to camp out.

However, the bears are there. Quite harmless, I was assured, though I noticed that the people who told me that—strong men, too—ran as though for their very lives when a bear suddenly started moving toward them.

One day we were watching one of the bears—you can see the very one in the picture—when someone said, "Look, he's going to get into that car."

Of course, everybody was excited and ran to see what would happen.

It seems that Mr. Bear had for some time made a

habit of visiting automobiles and removing anything and everything that looked good for food, usually ripping up the upholstery in the process. He was about to do the same again. Standing on the running board, he poked his great nose into the open window, while the crowd looked on and giggled.

One woman was most amused and laughed out loud, calling her friends to come and watch the fun.

Then something happened I shall never forget.

Suddenly a voice called out, "Say, the bear has been in that blue car over there. He's torn the back seat to ribbons and eaten a whole box of chocolates, box and all."

Everybody turned to look. There was a cry from

the woman who had been laughing so heartily a moment before.

"That's *my* car!" she exclaimed in mingled astonishment and anger.

It was—the upholstery was all torn, and her precious box of chocolates had vanished.

Rather hard luck, of course, but it did seem to me like a judgment on her, for she had not cared so long as it was somebody else's car that was damaged.

Then there came to my mind that old text in the book of Proverbs: "He that is glad at calamities shall not be unpunished." Proverbs 17:5.

It certainly came true then.

How very careful we should always be, when others suffer, not to make their burden heavier, for we never know how quickly the same disaster may befall us.

Sometimes, I have noticed, it comes very soon indeed.

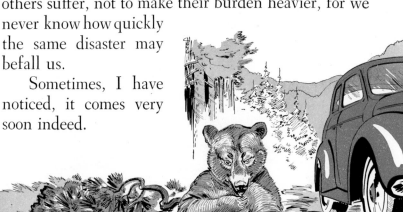

I remember once laughing at a friend because his car had broken down when climbing a steep hill. Within a very little while my own car had broken down from exactly the same trouble, and that same friend, of all people, was with me when it happened! How he could have jeered at my misfortune—but he didn't. Very good of him, wasn't it?

I hope you will always be like that. And when your friend—or your enemy—falls over, or gets a puncture in his bicycle tire, or drops his marble down a drain, or loses something else that is precious to him, don't stand by laughing, but lend a helping hand and speak a word of sympathy. Then someday, when your turn comes to suffer, perhaps there will be someone near by to run to your rescue and bring some hope and courage to your own sad heart.

# Ingratitude

*M*R. AND MRS. TOMLIN-
son lived on a lonely farm in the Middle West of
America. They had one son, whom they loved more
than life itself. He was everything to them, and all
that they had was reckoned only as a trust for him.

From the day Harold was born, Father and Mother
resolved that they would try to give him the very
best education possible. They thought maybe he might
become a doctor or a judge, or perhaps the President
of the United States. Anyhow, Harold should have his
chance.

How could it be done? It would cost money to
send the lad to college, much more than the farm
could yield in any one year. So right from the start they
began to save up.

As he sat by the fireside one evening, Father said,
"Mother, I've decided to give up my tobacco, and every
time I am tempted to send for an ounce or two, I'll take
the money and put it in that vase on the mantelpiece."

Startled but pleased, Mother thought awhile, and
presently, not to be outdone, she said:

"All right, dear, then I'll give up my tea, and every time I am tempted to send for a package, I'll take the money and put it in the same vase."

"Good!" said Father. "That's a bargain!"

So they made their compact, and the vase on the mantelpiece became their bank.

The years rolled by, years of hard work, patient toil, and desperate self-sacrifice. But they never murmured, for was it not all for Harold—dear, dear Harold—joy of their hearts?

Then at last the great day came when Harold was old enough to go to college. How proud they were of him, dressed in a fine new suit! How Mother wept over him at the thought of his going! How Father went around with a heart like lead!

Then they parted. The last farewells were said, the last kisses exchanged, and Harold was gone—over the hills and far, far away.

200

The leave-taking was particularly sad, because they would not see him for five long years. Every penny would be needed to keep the boy at college; so they didn't dare think of spending any on fares.

One year passed—two years. Then one day Father said he couldn't wait any longer.

"I must see the boy," he said. "He's been gone these two years now, and I can't wait another three."

"But remember how we need the money for him," said Mother.

"I know," replied Father, "but it won't cost anything. I'll take the old farm cart and drive the whole way myself, and sleep under haystacks and the stars at night."

"You can't do it," said Mother.

"I can," said Father. "I can do anything just to see our Harold."

So he went. Over those same hills and far away, driving on and on and on, weary to death sometimes, but his heart beating with ever-growing joy at the thought of meeting Harold.

At last, after many days, he drew near the university town where Harold was at college. He could see it in the distance, and even the horse seemed to bound forward with fresh eagerness. So near now, so soon to meet his son.

Now he was going down the main boulevard

toward the college buildings. It did seem funny to be driving an old farm cart along such a beautiful street; but what did he care? He was thinking only of Harold and the joy of meeting him again.

Where was he?

Father's old head was bobbing from side to side, his keen eyes searching every group of laughing young people with one absorbing objective—Harold.

Look!

Yes, surely that must be Harold, coming out of the main entrance hall with a crowd of jolly, carefree young men and women around him. How smart he looked, so tall and handsome! Pride surged through the old man's heart. This was his own dear boy grown to manhood, worth a thousand times all the sacrifice they had made for him.

"Harold!"

High above the chatter and laughter rose the old man's cry. How eager it was, how full to overflowing of a Father's love.

"Harold!"

Everybody heard it, and seeing the old farm cart in front of the college building, burst out laughing.

Harold heard it too. He turned, and his face paled. Not a smile greeted the old man. Harold was ashamed of his Father—sorry that his college friends should discover he came from such humble stock.

"Harold!" There was something plaintive in the voice this time. "Don't you know me, my boy?"

Yes, he knew, but he didn't want the others to know.

"You've made a mistake," he said coldly. "Better take that old contraption out of here."

Father's heart froze. Deathly pale, he turned the cart around, and amid the jeers of the onlookers, drove away. Back over the same long road he went, on and on, stunned and crushed, scarcely able to raise his head.

Mother saw him coming, and sensed at once that something was wrong. He seemed twenty years older.

Dismounting, and saying never a word, he went into the dining room and sat down in the old armchair near the mantelpiece, where the vase of sacrifice still stood, a silent witness to the price of love.

Realizing that something terrible must have happened, Mother went quietly about the house, preparing a meal, hoping that soon he would recover himself.

Suddenly an awful sound fell on her ears—a groan of anguish, followed by a thud of something falling.

She ran in, and there on the hearth lay Father, dead.

"Died of a broken heart," people said. "Killed by base ingratitude," was the true verdict.

Sad, terribly sad, wasn't it? Yet how often it happens that the tender love and patient sacrifice of parents are forgotten and despised by unworthy children.

I once told this story in a little church in Wales.

After the meeting an old, bearded man came up to me and said, "How true it is! This very thing happened in my own town not long ago. A Father I know lavished every kindness on his son, finally setting him up in business at great expense to himself. Then one day, after the son was doing well, the Father went in from the country to see him. The young man had some important business friends present at the time; so he whispered in his Father's ear, 'Don't let them know you are my Father.' It fairly broke the old man's heart, and within a few weeks he died."

Which makes me wonder how you are treating your parents. Are you ever ashamed of them? Do you honor them as you should for the love they have poured out on you? Have you ever thought how much money they might have had, how easy life might have been for them, but for you?

How you should love them now, ere it be forever too late; so that you may have no regrets after the great Reaper has passed and the old home is empty and desolate.

What does the Good Book say?

"Honour thy father and thy mother: that thy days may be long upon the land which the Lord Thy God giveth thee." Exodus 20:12.

WILLIAM F. YEAMES, R.A.

The Soldiers Were Searching for the Children's Daddy but Could Not Find Him. So They Questioned the Children
—"And When Did You Last See Your Daddy?" The Little Boy Stood Bravely Before Them and Would Not Tell

# Brave Boys

*N*OT LONG AGO TWO young boys were playing on the bank of a river. All of a sudden the smaller one fell in and was swept away by the current. Instantly, without a moment's thought for himself, the other boy jumped in to save his brother. Neither could swim, and both were drowned.

Terribly sad, wasn't it? But what a noble boy was that older brother!

Every day the papers tell us about brave boys—boys who jump into an icy pond to save a friend who has fallen in; boys who dash through a fire to save a baby sister; boys who stand up against bigger boys who are bullying at school.

In almost every boy there is a quality of bravery which somehow rises up within him in the moment of emergency.

Look at the little chap in the picture. His Father was a cavalier in the days of the great civil war in England. The Roundheads have captured the Father's castle, and are searching for the Father himself. They are very anxious to find him, for he is an important man, and his capture will mean much to them.

Everyone in the castle is questioned as to the knight's whereabouts, but no one seems to know. Then one of the soldiers has a bright idea. "Ask the children," he suggests. "If they know, they will surely tell."

So the two children are sent for. They are terribly frightened, and the poor Mother is even more afraid, for she does not know what the children will say. But the boy is very brave. He doesn't say a word.

The soldiers ask him, "And when did you last see your Father?" But he will not reply. Nothing will persuade him to betray his Daddy. How proud his Mother must have been that day!

But boys can be as brave today as ever they were in the days of old.

Some years ago, in the Rocky Mountains, a busload of happy children left their school one day and

started on their homeward journey. It was wintertime and snow was falling. They had not gone more than a few miles when the bus became stuck in a snowdrift and would not move either forward or backward.

Just then a terrible blizzard descended from the mountains, and the bus was soon covered with snow. The driver did his best to keep the children warm. At first he got them to tear up all their schoolbooks and notebooks, and with these he made a fire in a tin can, round which they crowded for warmth. When all the books were gone, they broke up the wooden seats and fed the fire with these.

At last the fire went out, and the driver tried to keep the children warm by getting them to box and wrestle, sing and dance. They managed to keep themselves alive all through the afternoon, evening, and night, until the morning; but then they found that one poor little girl had died.

At this the brave driver decided to go out and search for help. But the snow was so deep and the blizzard so fierce that he lost his way, fell in the snow, and died.

Before he left the bus he had told one of the older boys, Bryan Untiedt, that he must take charge and keep the children awake at all costs. Bryan was only thirteen at the time, but he rose to the occasion and showed a heroism that stirred the world.

The children were now all huddled together at the

4-14

back of the bus. Suddenly it was noticed that yet another one had died of the awful cold. This made the children frantic, and in the excitement one of them broke a window, and thus left them wide open to the wind and snow. Bryan

Bryan Untiedt With President Hoover

tried to keep up their spirits, and started the boxing and wrestling again. But they were all getting exhausted now, and could not keep it up for long.

Noticing that his own little brother had become unconscious, this dear brave lad actually took off all his own clothes, save only his underclothes, and wrapped them around his brother. But the little brother died also, and then they all, one by one, fell down on the floor of the bus and lost consciousness.

It was not until late that afternoon that a farmer stumbled accidentally upon the bus. He was horrified to find the heap of unconscious children inside, and as fast as he could he carried them to his home. Many did not recover, but Bryan was soon well again. For his bravery he was sent for by President Hoover and entertained several days at the White House.

210

Not all brave deeds are noticed and written about in the papers as was this one. Many are done out of sight, and only God sees them. Yet some of these are the bravest of all.

It is a brave deed to speak the truth when it may bring us suffering. When teacher asks at school, "Who has been talking while I've been out of the room?" it is a brave deed to hold up your hand if you are guilty, and say, "I did, sir."

The teacher may look very solemnly at you, and tell you to stay in for half an hour after school, but in his heart he will admire you for your honesty and courage.

It is a brave deed to resist a temptation to do wrong. When someone would lead you to steal or to lie or to swear, and you say, "I cannot do that," you have done a very noble deed—one that takes more courage sometimes than jumping into a river to rescue a drowning friend.

It is a brave deed also to refuse to laugh when the laughter would cause suffering to others; or to refuse to laugh at an unholy jest or an impure story. The boy who can turn away at such a time, or better still say, "Stop it, boys; this isn't right," is brave indeed.

The world needs more brave boys like these. There is room for them everywhere. They are wanted at school, on the playground, and in all the great battles of life. God bless them!

# The Story of Trains

*H*OW EASY AND CON-
venient it is for us to travel about nowadays! Of course,
I know that sometimes the trains are crowded and sometimes they do not arrive on time; but, really, taking
everything into consideration, aren't we much better
off than the people who lived a hundred years or so
ago? Those who lived in the country had to stay in the
country. There were no seaside holidays for them,
unless they were rich. And if they lived at the seaside,
they had to stay there, for there were no trains to take
them into the country.

Suppose there were no trains today! Of course, it
would save us a great deal of worry trying to catch
them; but, really, it would be very awkward, after all.
We know something of what it would be like, because
in some parts of the world there have been railway
strikes. During a strike all the men who work the
engines and pull the signals down stop work. But a
hundred and forty years ago the whole country was
just like that the whole time—not a locomotive was
to be seen anywhere.

The fact is that in those days nobody knew how to make a steam engine properly. A man by the name of George Stephenson had the idea in his mind and was trying to work it out, but that is as far as the locomotive had advanced.

It was in the year 1814, the year before the Battle of Waterloo, when Stephenson was only thirty-three years old, that he made his first engine. He called it the *Blucher,* and it succeeded in hauling a train of eight loaded cars, weighing thirty tons, at a speed of four miles an hour.

Every year after that saw improvements and an increase in power and speed. In 1825 a railway line was laid between Stockton and Darlington, England, and though at first the managers thought they would have the coaches pulled by horses, Stephenson persuaded them to use his locomotives. The first train on this railway was composed of thirty-four cars, weighing in all ninety tons. It started off at about ten miles an hour, and even reached fifteen miles an hour, which was a terrific speed in those days. Indeed, the people were so scared about it that a signalman on horseback was sent in front of the engine to make sure that no one would get run over!

Three weeks after this line was opened, a regular daily passenger service was started. Each passenger was allowed to carry only fourteen pounds of baggage.

Four years later, in 1829, the directors of the Liverpool and Manchester Railway, whose line was then under construction, offered a prize of $2,500 for the best locomotive. There were three entries, Stephenson's *Rocket* and two others. These latter two broke down during the trials, but the *Rocket* drew a train weighing thirteen tons thirty-five miles in forty-eight minutes, an average speed of nearly forty-four miles an hour. Up to that time, this was the fastest that man had ever traveled. People were more excited over this than we are when we hear of a plane going faster than sound.

So successful was this line between Liverpool and Manchester that numerous other railways were soon begun all over the country. By 1840 there were 1,331 miles of track laid down. For the next ten years there was a railway mania, and by the year 1850 more than 6,600 miles had been laid. During the next fifty years

Stephenson's Prize
"Rocket," 1829

this increased to 21,855 miles. Today it is much more than that.

In the United States a railway was started in 1826, the engines for it being brought over from England. Canada, however, had no railways until 1853. Most of the countries of Europe had some working by that time, but Turkey and Greece delayed until 1860 and 1869. Africa's first railway (1856) was from Alexandria to Cairo; Asia's (1853), from Bombay to Tannah; Australia's, a line in Victoria in 1854.

Nowadays there are some very long railways in existence. The Canadian Pacific, for instance, runs right across the American continent, a distance of 2,906 miles. But the longest of all in the world is the Trans-Siberian Railway from Leningrad to Vladivostok, nearly 6,000 miles.

### SUBWAYS, OR "TUBES"

So much for the trains that run on the surface of the earth. How about those that run underground? Who planned and started them? And how long have they been there?

Nobody thought of making subways until people began to crowd into the great cities. When it became clear that the busses and "trams," or streetcars, of London could not possibly carry all the people who wanted to travel about the city, somebody struck upon the idea of diverting some of the traffic underground. In the year 1853 the first underground railway was begun from Edgware Road to King's Cross.

In those days people did not know how to make tunnels as well as they do nowadays; so the way they built the greater part of that first tube was like this: Along the route that the railway was to follow, a wide, deep trench was dug, then the sides and roof of the tunnel were built of brick, after which earth was filled in and the surface of the ground restored. Streets and houses were then built on top.

Thirty-three years later another tube was started, which came to be known as the "City and South London Railway." The builder, whose name was Greathead, introduced a new method of construction, which enabled him to cut a circular hole ten feet in diameter at a depth of forty to eighty feet below the surface. In this method a shield is employed, which holds up the earth during excavation, gives room for the building of the permanent walls, and is pushed forward as the digging proceeds. With this method there was, of course, no interference with the surface of the streets during construction, except at the shafts, which were sunk where the stations were to be located.

The cars on this line were so shaped as to fit closely to the size of the tunnel, it being expected that the trains would act as pistons, driving the stale air in front of them up the station shaft ahead and drawing fresh air down the shaft behind. Experience proved, however, that this did not happen; the stale air remained and kept out the fresh. Anyone who traveled on that railway before it was remodeled will remember the strange, musty smell that pervaded it.

Many other subways have since been constructed, and the foundations of many great cities are now literally honeycombed with underground railways. New York, Chicago, and Philadelphia have them. Some of the companies at first used steam engines to draw the trains; but steam and smoke underground were too much for the passengers. Fortunately all these lines have now been electrified.

Building subways is a very costly business, much more so than building railways above ground. The deep tunnels cost on an average at least $1,000,000 a mile, and the "cut and cover" method of the Metropolitan Railway in London reached as high as $5,000,000 a mile, where large buildings had to be supported and a network of drains and sewers readjusted.

The only reason why we can travel on these railways so cheaply is that vast numbers of people are carried. Hundreds of thousands of people travel about New York every day by subway; and if they pay only ten cents each, the total amount received by the owners is very large.

We have become so used to railways above ground and underground that we treat them as a matter of course, thinking nothing of all the labor and expense involved in building them, or of the great convenience they are to us. But, really, when you come to think of it, it is wonderful that we should be able to travel almost anywhere so easily and so cheaply.

Just think how surprised and pleased Daniel and old King Nebuchadnezzar would be if they could wake up this evening and ride in the *Super Chief* between Los Angeles and Chicago! Wouldn't they just rub their

eyes! Imagine their going down the stairs in Lower Manhattan, entering a subway train, and in a few moments coming up in Jersey City, on the other side of the Hudson

River! I think Daniel would begin to think that his prophecy was being fulfilled about men running "to and fro" and knowledge being increased in the last days. (Daniel 12:4.)

And that makes me think of Isaiah, another prophet. He said that one day "every valley" would be exalted, and "every mountain and hill" would be made low, that the crooked places would be made straight, and the rough places plain. Just think of his traveling over the great iron roads of the world for hundreds of thousands of miles, across valleys and through mountains, on a straight, smooth surface! Don't you think he would see in this the fulfillment of his prophecy, especially when he knew that every year millions of copies of the Bible and thousands of missionaries were being carried on these railways to the very ends of the earth to make known "the glory of the Lord"? (See Isaiah 40:3-5.)

Truly this is the most wonderful time in all the history of the world. Children of today are more blessed than those of any other age. Don't you think we should be the happiest people who ever lived?

# Turned to Stone

*A*REN'T YOU GOING TO say your prayers tonight?" asked Mamma, as Dick sulkily jumped into bed.

"No, I don't want to say my prayers," answered Dick abruptly.

"Dick!" exclaimed Mamma aghast. "I'm surprised at you. Whatever can have happened to you lately? You used to love to say your prayers."

"The other fellows at school don't say theirs," replied Dick. "They say it's all nonsense."

"That's what I was afraid of," said Mamma. "Those boys you're going with nowadays aren't doing you any good. Why do you let them influence you so? It's quenching all the love you once had for Jesus and turning your little heart to stone. By the way, did you ever see anything being turned to stone?"

"No."

"Well, I have. At Matlock Bath, in Derbyshire, there are remarkable springs of water coming out of the earth that will turn things to stone within a year. An enterprising man who lives there prepared a big tank

in which for many years he has been putting all sorts
of things for the water to work upon. There you can
see birds' nests and eggs, sponges, walking sticks, boots,
even a man's hat, so covered with a limestone crust that
they look for all the world as if they were made of
stone. But there is one very remarkable thing to notice,
if ever you go there, Dick. All around that tank are
green ferns and moss and tiny bushes, but not one of
them is turned to stone, although the same water
splashes over them. Can you think why?"

"No, I can't," said Dick.

"Then I'll tell you," said Mamma. "It is because
they are alive. The water turns only dead things to
stone. It has no power whatever over living things."

"But what has that to do with me?"

"Everything. That water resembles the influence of the other boys at school. You cannot help its splashing over you, but you can keep it from harming you, from turning your heart to stone."

"I don't see how I can," said Dick.

"By keeping your heart alive," said Mamma. "Like those plants you must keep in touch with the source of life, or something will die inside you and you will become just a hardened little worldling like the others."

Dick was silent now, evidently thinking.

"And you know the Source of life, just as well as I do," said Mamma. "It is Jesus. And only as we keep in touch with Him by saying our prayers and reading the Bible and going to church to listen to the preaching of His Word, can we draw life from Him to keep our own hearts green and living."

They talked like this for half an hour or so. Then Dick began to crawl out of bed.

"I think I'll say my prayers tonight, after all," he said. "Mamma, you're right."

# Just Twenty Minutes

*H*ERE IS A VERY RE-
markable prayer experience that happened to a friend
of mine not long ago.

He has a large family and needs a great deal of
money to keep everything going week by week.

Sometimes he wonders how he will make ends
meet; but always, just when things look darkest, a light
shines through. His wonderful faith in Jesus is always
wonderfully rewarded.

On one occasion, not long ago, he needed sixty
dollars for taxes—not very much to a wealthy man, but
a huge sum to this poor farmer.

And he had to have it by a certain time—the next
Monday morning.

Over and over he thought of his problem. How
could he get sixty dollars by Monday morning? It
seemed impossible.

He thought of his cows. Yes. He would be willing
to sell one of them to raise the money, but nobody was
buying cows at this time. In fact, no cow buyer had
been to his farm for months. There seemed no way out.

What could he do?

In his heart he believed that the dear Lord whom he loved would do something for him, but how or when, he could not think.

Sunday morning came, the last day before he had to pay the taxes. He rose, as usual, at three o'clock and went out to the dairy to milk the cows.

Returning just before six, he decided to take a brief nap to refresh himself for the rest of the day's tasks. Before doing so, however, he reminded the Lord that this was the day he needed that sixty dollars.

At six o'clock he lay down, and in a few moments was fast asleep. But he didn't sleep long.

Bang, bang, bang!

Someone was knocking on the window.

Startled, my farmer friend awoke, jumped from his bed, and demanded to know what was the matter. For the moment he was too dazed to know how long he had slept, but supposed it must now be eight o'clock at least.

"Sorry to disturb you," said his plowman, "but there's a man here wants to speak to you."

"About what?"

"Wants to buy a cow."

The farmer was at the door in a moment, his heart beating fiercely with excitement which he dared not show.

Outside he found a man who lived several miles from his farm, and whom he had seen occasionally before.

"Sorry to bother you so early," said the man, "but I'm needing one more cow to complete a carload. Spent all yesterday searching for one in vain. Then I thought of you. Do you have one to sell?"

"It so happens that I have," said the farmer. "Come and look at it."

They went to the barn.

"How much do you want for it?" asked the visitor.

"Well," said the farmer hesitatingly, "I hardly know what to say. I don't know

4-15

what the market price is today, but I do know that I badly need sixty dollars for it."

Without a word the visitor took out his checkbook, wrote a check for sixty dollars, and prepared to depart with the cow.

"By the way," said the farmer, "when did you think about coming to see me about a cow?"

"This morning," said the visitor. "At six o'clock I was strongly impressed that you would have a cow to sell me, and that I should come and see you. So I got into my car and drove straight here."

"What is the time now?" asked the farmer.

"Six-twenty."

"Only six-twenty!" exclaimed the farmer. "Amazing! Perfectly amazing."

It was. It had taken just twenty minutes for his prayer to be answered.

# Ben's Loyalty

*A*T THE END OF THE lawn, where it merged into the wild patch of trees and bushes, stood Margie's playhouse. Her Father had made it for her, and she was never so happy as when she could be in it all alone with Ben.

Ben, of course, was her dog—a beautiful shepherd dog, who was devoted to his five-year-old mistress. They played so happily together, Ben watching all the time to see that no harm came to Margie.

Then one day, as Margie was walking through the garden to the playhouse, she heard a strange rattling noise. She could not remember having heard anything like it before, and she looked around, wondering what it could be. Then she walked on, but a moment later the same rattling noise came again, only louder and nearer this time.

Then something happened.

All of a sudden Ben, who had been walking near by, flashed across in front of Margie, and in a moment a terrific fight was in progress.

Terrified, Margie rushed back to the house.

"Mamma, Mamma!" she cried. "Ben's in a fight. Come quick, come quick!"

Mother hurried out and soon saw what was the matter. Ben had his teeth in a rattlesnake. Over and over they rolled. It was terrible to watch.

Just then Father came on the scene with a hoe in his hand and began hacking at the snake as best he could. At last the battle was over and the snake lay dead.

Then Father took Ben in his arms and began to look him over. He found three bites, two on his mouth, one on his head.

"He can look after those on his mouth," he said, "but I'm afraid of the other one. He can't lick that."

Gallant Ben, exhausted, lay down, licking away at the wounds on his mouth. Soon his head began to swell, and it got bigger and bigger until it didn't look like a dog's head at all.

Father came back to look at him, Margie, weeping and very frightened, at his side.

"Will he get better, Daddy?" she asked.

Father looked Ben over again.

"There's not much hope. Unless Jesus does something special for your pet, Margie, and very soon, I'm afraid we shall have to say good-by to him."

Margie ran indoors, and kneeling beside her bed, poured out her little heart to God.

"O dear Jesus," she pleaded, "my dear Ben was so brave looking after me, and the naughty snake bit him,

and now he's so very, very sick. Daddy says he's going to die if you don't do something quick. So please do something quick as you can, for I can't spare him. Please, Jesus, do."

By and by Margie went back to see Ben, taking some fresh water for him to drink. She found him still alive and the swelling definitely smaller.

"Come, Daddy!" she cried, running into the house. "Ben's getting better. He really is. Come and see." Father went and could hardly believe his eyes. Ben was indeed better, and within a week or so he had fully recovered.

Margie told me that she has never doubted, all the years since this happened, that Jesus answered her prayer.

I too think He did; don't you?

# A Noise in the Night

*T*HIS HAPPENED IN
August, 1939. It's about a Mother and her three children. They lived with an old grandfather, and they had very little of this world's goods.

Although the grandfather hadn't much use for religion, the Mother and the three girls all loved the Lord Jesus. And that was really what started it.

You see, the Mother wanted to take her three daughters to a camp meeting, where they would hear more about Jesus, but there was no money to pay the railway fare or to take care of their expenses while there. Grandpa laughed at the idea.

"Better put that nonsense out of your heads," he said. "You know you can't afford to go; so drop it."

But Mother didn't drop it. Instead, she prayed—and the girls prayed too—asking Jesus to help them do this thing that they thought would please Him, and to make it possible, somehow, for them to go.

The last night came. Still there was no money and no possibility of going.

"There's no use fretting," said grandpa. "You can't

go; so just forget it. Anyway, if God wants you to go, as you say, why doesn't He give you some evidence of it?"

Mother and the girls said their prayers once more, and retired for the night. Soon they were sound asleep. The hours slipped by. If anything was going to happen, it had to happen soon, or they would not be able to leave in the morning, as they had hoped and prayed and planned.

Something did happen.

At 3:30 A.M. Doris woke up with a start and sat bolt upright in bed.

There was an uncanny scratching noise coming from outside the front door.

Her sisters heard it and awoke.

Mother heard it and sat up, frightened and wondering. She listened intently.

The scratching continued, getting louder.

Doris got out of bed and cautiously approached the door. Opening it, she peered out into the darkness.

Two cats were scratching on the screen door!

Doris pushed the screen open, and then, to her amazement, she saw two packages lying on the porch.

"Mother, come," she cried, "there's something here!"

Mother jumped out of bed to see what it was all about, and discovered, not only two bulky packages, but four envelopes also.

Feverishly the packages and the envelopes were opened. In one package they found lunch for their journey, all neatly prepared; in the other was more food that they might need. Then in the four envelopes there was money for Mother and each of the three girls.

They were all so excited and overjoyed that they didn't sleep another wink that night. And was grandpa surprised when

they eagerly told him the story at breakfast time!

But who sent the parcels? Nobody knows. However, there was an anonymous note in one of the packages (I have the note) which read as follows:

"From a friend who wishes you a safe journey and a good spiritual time. May God watch over you and care for you until you return safe home, is my prayer for you."

Now, who sent that note?

Someone, I am sure, with a very tender heart—one of those dear people whom God uses now and then to answer His children's prayers.

234

# Two Girls and a Doll

*T*HIS IS A DOLL STORY; so boys may turn over the page if they want to. But, of course, if nobody's looking, they may read on.

It happened in Peru, South America, not long ago.

At a certain mission station there lived a sweet little girl called Jean. She was the missionary's daughter, and on her return with her family from their last furlough she had brought with her a most beautiful baby doll.

What a doll it was! One of those very modern ones that not only open and close their eyes, but say "Mamma" and "Papa" and do all sorts of other very delightful things besides. In fact, it was as near like a real baby as it could be without actually wriggling about on its own.

Of course the other little girls around were green with envy. The Peruvian children would stand and stare openeyed and openmouthed as Barbara—the doll —performed for them.

One of these girls, whom I will call Anita, was especially fascinated with Barbara, and in her little

heart she longed to have a baby doll like that. Again
and again she would go to her Father and ask him to
buy her one.

"Daddy," she would say, "won't you please get me
a doll like the one the missionary's little girl has?"

"I'm afraid I'll never be able to do that," said her
Father. "I do not have the money. It would take months
for me to save enough to buy a doll like that, and we
need so many other things first."

Anita was disappointed, but she refused to believe
that she could never have a doll like Barbara.

Then she thought of Jesus, and took the burden
of her heart to Him.

"Please, dear Jesus," she would say, "you know
how I long for a beautiful doll like the one the missionary's little girl has. If you can give her one, couldn't you

236

give me one as well? My own dolly is such a poor little thing beside hers. Please send me one somehow."

So she prayed and hoped, but no dolly came.

Her Father heard about her prayer and told her not to be disappointed if it was not answered. It was so impossible, he said. Still Anita prayed on.

One day she said to her Father, "I know my dolly's coming soon. I feel it all over me. I'm sure it's coming. I believe it will come today."

"No, darling. I'm afraid not," said her Father; "it is too much to hope for."

Just then they looked up and saw Jean, the missionary's daughter, coming toward their home, with Barbara, big and beautiful, clasped tightly in her arms.

"There she is," said Anita. "Isn't she lovely? I want one just like that."

Just then there was a knock at the door.

"I've come to see Anita," said Jean, with a heavenly smile on her pretty face.

Anita ran to greet her.

"O Anita," said Jean, "I have wanted to see you so much all day. You see, Daddy's just been called back home. And we all have to go right away. So this morn-

ing I thought about you and, and—er—and Barbara. Would you be ever so good to Barbara if I were to give her to you?"

"Give her to me!" exclaimed Anita. "To keep for my very own?"

"Yes," said Jean, "for your very, very own."

"How good and kind of you," said Anita; "but what about you?"

"Oh, I'm so happy to give her to you, and Daddy says that someday he'll get me another one."

"Thank you, thank you a million times," cried Anita, hugging Barbara in her arms. Then, looking up at her Daddy, she said, "I told you so, Daddy. It was not impossible. I knew Jesus would answer my prayer. He always does, you know."

238

# Found in the Snow

*B*OBBY WAS THREE
years old, getting on toward four.

He must have been descended from some famous explorer, for he was always searching into things to find out just what they were like.

One day when his Daddy was going to a small village up in the mountains near his home, he decided to take Bobby along with him. Bobby was delighted. He loved going out with Daddy for trips in his car.

They arrived at last at the village, and Daddy went into the main store to attend to some business he had there.

Bobby, left alone in the car, began to look around. He thought the little village, perched up there in the mountains, was a very pretty place. Through the trees higher up he could see some white stuff on the ground. Maybe this was what people called snow. He thought he would like to get some; so he opened the car door and jumped out.

He would easily be back before Daddy got through with his business, he thought—for Daddy was away

dreadfully long sometimes.
So off he trotted along
the rough wagon road that
seemed to lead upward to-
ward the snow.

But the snow was far-
ther away than Bobby
thought, and the uphill
climb was steep for little
legs. He quite forgot that
Daddy might be getting
anxious about him.

As for Daddy, he was panic-stricken. Coming out
of the store at last, he found the car empty. Bobby had
disappeared!

He called and called him, running hither and
yon, but no Bobby answered. He asked everybody
around, but no one had seen a little boy anywhere.

"Kidnaped!" thought poor Daddy in despair. He
phoned his home, then the police. In a few hours two
hundred people were searching.

But no Bobby could they find. All night long they
tried to discover some clue as to where he might be,
but in vain.

Daddy didn't go to bed for he couldn't sleep a
wink. He was desperate, worried to death as to what
might have happened to his precious little son.

Morning came, and still no word of Bobby.

The people searched on. Someone found marks left by Bobby's shoes in the wagon road, but nobody dreamed that he would have walked up the mountain.

Afternoon came. Most people had given up hope by now. If he had been kidnaped, then there was no use searching the district; if he had wandered into the woods, then he must have died of cold before this.

But Daddy refused to give up. As a last effort he decided to follow the wagon road as far as it would take him.

On and on he went, one mile, two miles, three miles, four miles. It seemed useless. There was snow up at this level. He might as well turn back. Anyway, night would soon be falling again. Thirty hours had passed since Bobby was lost.

Then his terrible sorrow and helplessness made him turn to God.

"Oh, dear Lord," he cried, dropping on his knees, "if my little boy is up here, show me where he is, please, before it gets dark again." Again and again he repeated his prayer in dreadful agony of soul.

All of a sudden he heard a faint cry. At first he thought it was a bird. Then, looking up, he saw Bobby lying face down in a patch of muddy, melting snow.

Leaping to the little boy's side, Daddy picked him up and ran with him in his arms down toward the village. Halfway down the hill he met the other searchers, and how happy they were that Bobby had been found! All hurried on to the village store to Bobby's Mother, who nearly collapsed with relief when they brought him in. A doctor said Bobby was uninjured and would soon recover from his cold, lonely night on the mountainside.

As for Daddy, he doesn't know how to be thankful enough that God answered his prayer so wonderfully, before it got dark again.

# When Louise Ran Away

*T*HAT STORY ABOUT
Bobby reminds me of Louise. She is just a little bit of a
baby girl, between two and three, but so very sweet and
dear, with the loveliest golden, curly hair and bright,
sparkling eyes.

I loved her the moment I saw her, and so would
you, if you could see her. Then her Mother told me
this story about her.

Not long ago little Louise decided, all on her own,
that she would like to go out and see the world.

Now, when little girls of two or three, or even four
or five, decide to do any such thing, they really should
ask Mamma or Daddy first; otherwise it makes for such
a great deal of trouble.

Well, one day Louise walked out of the house, and
wandered on down the street, looking in people's
houses and gardens, talking to other children, and
generally enjoying life very much.

After a while, however, she thought she would
go back to see her Mamma; but she suddenly realized
that she did not know where she was.

Very much frightened, she began to call.

"Mamma! Mamma!"

But no Mamma came. Louise started to run, but unfortunately, though she did not know it, she was running away from home instead of toward it.

Meanwhile, Mamma, who had supposed Louise was in the garden, had noticed the strange silence everywhere and had gone out to see what could be the matter.

Her precious baby girl was nowhere to be seen.

Mother ran to the neighbors. No, they had not seen Louise, but they would help look for her, they said. Soon a number of people were looking.

Daddy, wild with anxiety, called the police, and then, jumping in his car, dashed up and down the streets at top speed, hoping every minute that he would find her.

Suddenly, half a mile from home, as he neared the main highway, he spotted a little figure running for all she was worth, and screaming, "I want my Mamma! I want my Mamma!"

244

It was Louise.

Daddy grabbed her up in his arms and drove her home in triumph.

Then Mamma and Daddy and Louise had a little session together; that is, after the neighbors had all gone home, and the police had been told that everything was all right now.

And Mamma told Louise how naughty it was for little girls to run away like this, and how much trouble and worry it caused; and Daddy said she might have been killed if she had run just a little farther on to the highway.

Then Louise, looking very sad, promised that she would never, *never,* NEVER run away again.

She told me the same thing the other day, bless her heart; so I'm sure she never will.

# Tangled Threads

*J*MET A KIND LADY
one day who told me that she had been a nurse for many
years in the hospital of a large orphan home. What
stories she had to tell! Here is one about a poor little
boy called Willie.

Willie was lying there in his bed very quietly and
very patiently, with nothing much to do until his next
meal should be brought in. Nurse was busy moving to
and fro, caring for the needs of her large family and
keeping a watchful eye on all. She loved every one of
them, even though they did make her very, very tired.

Now as Willie turned his head from side to side,
looking at the other children and watching nurse hurrying about, he caught sight of one of his stockings re-
posing upon the chair beside his bed. Why he should
suddenly become interested in this stocking I do not
know, but he did. Perhaps it was because there was a
small hole in the knee and a piece of wool was dangling
down.

Willie put out his hand, drew the stocking over in
front of him, and began pulling at the loose thread.

You can guess what happened. The thread gave and became longer and longer in Willie's hand. It was the best bit of fun he had had for a long time, and he pulled and pulled and pulled at it.

Soon there was a hole big enough to put his whole knee through, and all around him, crisscrossing over the bed, were yards and yards of gray wool.

He was still gaily pulling away when a voice from the other end of the ward arrested him.

"Willie! what are you doing?"

"Just playing with my stocking," said Willie innocently.

"Just playing with your stocking!" exclaimed nurse,  moving swiftly to his bedside. "At this rate you won't have any stocking at all in a few minutes. It's too bad of you, Willie. I could have mended that other hole for you in a few moments, but this one will take hours. And you know how terribly busy I am."

"I'm sorry," said Willie, "I didn't mean

to. I don't want to make you tired; really I don't."

"But what's the use of saying that now?" reflected nurse. "The mischief's all done."

At this point Willie had a bright and beautiful idea.

"Nurse," he said, "don't worry. I'll put it all back again. Lend me your knitting needles."

Nurse smiled. "You couldn't mend it," she said.

"Yes, I can," said Willie confidently. "You let me have your needles, and see what I can do."

Nurse knew it was hopeless, but she loved the little chap for his willingness to try to put right the wrong he had done. So she brought him her knitting needles and left him to do his best.

Poor Willie! How he tried! Of course he didn't have the faintest idea how to use the needles, but he did his best, moving them to and fro, round and round, up and down, in a vain attempt to make the wool go back where it had been.

The result, as you can imagine, was funny beyond words. It looked like a bird's nest. The tangle was terrible.

Nurse came at last. There were tears in Willie's eyes. He realized he had failed.

"I'm sorry," he wept. "I've tried so hard to put it back again."

Nurse bent over and kissed him.

"Don't worry, Willie. I'll fix it after you've gone to sleep tonight."

And she did.

And she said to me, "Isn't it just like that with all of us? We make a mistake, and then try to get ourselves out of it; and the more we try, the more tangled we get until we don't know just what to do. Then we give up and put the whole tangled mess into the hands of Jesus, the Master Knitter, and ask Him to put it straight, and fix things as they were before. And in His own wonderful way, He does."

What a lovely thought from Willie's worn-out stocking!

Let's try to remember it, shall we, next time things go wrong?

# Saved From an Earthquake

*H*ERE IS A TRUE STORY of the wonderful way Jesus cares for His children in the midst of the worst disasters.

It happened over in Japan at the time of the great earthquake in 1923. Perhaps you have heard about that dreadful happening, when two great cities were wiped out, and nearly a quarter of a million people were killed, many thousands being burned to death after the earthquake had brought the houses all tumbling down upon them.

Living there at the time, on the outskirts of Tokyo, was a missionary family. Father was the minister of a little Christian church, and Mother, well, she was almost everything else, including the organist.

Now, because they were both so busy at the church, they usually left their little baby girl at home during services. She must have been a very good baby, because she slept peacefully in her baby carriage until Father and Mother came home.

On the morning of the great earthquake, however, baby would not sleep. She was restless and disturbed, and nothing would quiet her. As the time for meeting approached, poor Father and Mother found themselves in a most awkward fix, and didn't know what to do. For Father had to go to preach the sermon, and Mother had to go to play the organ; so what was to be done with baby? They couldn't leave her behind crying, and yet how could they take her to church in such a restless mood?

When there was hardly a moment left, they decided to take baby along and make the best of it.

They did so, and the service proceeded very much as usual until the last hymn had been sung.

Then came the first awful rumbling of the approaching earthquake. Everybody rushed outside, just in time to see the building opposite crash to the ground. Looking toward the city, they saw the smoke of a hundred fires. All around buildings began to topple over.

HERBERT
RUDEEN

Naturally they thought of their own home. What had happened to it? They ran off to see.

It was still standing. Only the big brick chimney had fallen.

Father pushed his way inside, searching for the baby's carriage, so that he could put her in it.

At first he could not see it, and wondered what could possibly have happened to it while they had been away. Then he saw something that made his face grow pale. The baby carriage, crushed flat as a pancake, was buried beneath the ruins of the chimney!

Had baby not been so restless that morning, she would have been killed instantly with the first shock of the earthquake.

Somehow I feel that the angels were watching over that dear child that day. How anxiously they must have tried to keep her from sleeping! And how glad they must have been when they saw Father and Mother take her away to church!

Jesus does look after His own, doesn't He?

And I know the story is true, for I met that baby the other day, now grown up into a fine, lovely girl. And as I looked at her, I wondered what great destiny the Lord has in store for her, seeing He saved her so wonderfully from the earthquake.

We need His protection, too, so let us pray this sweet little prayer to Him tonight:

"Jesus, Friend of little children,
    Be a Friend to me;
Take my hand and ever keep me
    Close to Thee.

"Step by step, O lead me onward,
    Upward into youth;
Wiser, stronger, still becoming
    In Thy truth.

"Never leave me nor forsake me,
    Ever be my friend;
For I need Thee from life's dawning
    To its end."

# A Chick Tragedy

*N*OW, BILLY AND BUNTY were two very little boys, just old enough to know that when Mamma said no she meant no, and that when she said yes, well, everything was all right.

Just now they were bothering Mamma a bit in the kitchen, trying to float bits of sticks in the sink, and things like that, until at last Mamma sent them helter-skelter into the garden.

"You can play anywhere you like," said Mamma, throwing their ball out to them, "but do be good. And mind, whatever you do, don't let the baby chicks out."

"All right, Mamma," said the boys. "We'll be very good."

"May we go and look at the baby chicks?"

"Oh, yes," said Mamma, "but don't open the door of their run."

"All right, Mamma," said Billy and Bunty, running onto the lawn with their ball.

For quite a long time they played very happily together on the grass. Then they began to wander slowly down the garden toward the chickens. There

254

were lots of things to interest them on the way. A big
furry caterpillar was crawling over a cabbage leaf. A
little sparrow was trying to take a bath in a puddle in
the path. Billy and Bunty watched them with great
interest.

By the time they reached the house where the baby
chicks were kept, they had quite forgotten all that
Mamma had said to them.

"What dear little
things!" said Billy.

"They look all fluffy,
like baby pussycats,"
said Bunty.

"I'd like to stroke
one, wouldn't you?" said
Billy.

"Yes," said Bunty,
"let's try to catch one."

So they opened the
door and stretched in
their little arms as far as
they would go. Bunty
caught one first.

"Now get one for
me," said Billy.

Bunty passed his over
to Billy and made another

grab. He caught another. Then they stood together, stroking their little pets and feeling very happy.

After a while they got tired of this and popped the baby chicks back into their house. Then they strolled leisurely up the garden again, played ball on the lawn, and at last arrived at the kitchen door about suppertime, ready for a good meal.

"So here you are again, darlings," said Mamma. "You have been good boys all the afternoon!"

"Yes, Mamma," said Billy and Bunty, "we've been very good boys."

Then they had their supper and went to bed.

In the morning, when Mamma came back from feeding the chickens, she had a very sad look on her face. Very sad indeed.

"There are two baby chicks dead," she said.

"Oh dear!" said Billy and Bunty together. "What a pity!"

"Yes," said Mamma. "Someone must have left the door of their house open. They must have hopped out, and then not been able to get back again. They must have just died of the cold."

"Poor baby chicks!" said the boys.

Billy looked at Bunty and Bunty looked at Billy. They seemed to remember something about it.

Mamma noticed the look.

"I suppose you didn't touch the chicken house yesterday afternoon?" she said.

Again Billy looked at Bunty and Bunty looked at Billy. They were very quiet. A big tear jumped out of the corner of Bunty's eye, and Billy looked very sad.

"I think you were very naughty little boys," said Mamma.

"We're very sorry," said Billy.

"And we won't do it any more," said Bunty.

"I'm afraid I shall have to——" began Mamma.

But before she could say just what she was going to do, two pairs of arms were thrown round her neck, and two little tearful voices were pleading for forgiveness.

And, well, what could Mamma do then?

So they went down the garden and buried the baby chicks behind the berry bushes.

4-17

The World Is Full of Curious Things. They Are All About Us. Yes, There Might
Be Some in Your Own Back Yard or Garden. It's Fun to Look for Them

# Curiosities

*H*UNTING FOR CURI-
osities is a great game. It will keep you amused for hours. That is, of course, if you find some now and then to encourage your effort.

Perhaps you will say, "What is a curiosity?" Well, it is something different from the ordinary, like a stone with a hole in it on the beach. There are millions of pebbles on the beach, but only a few of them have holes. That's why we like to find them, isn't it?

Of course, if you live near the seaside, you can find all sorts of curiosities if you start to search for them. Strange shells, starfish, anemones, and funny little bits of seaweed.

If you live in the country, there are curiosities without number in the fields and woods—quaint little birds, peculiar flowers, hollow trees, and the like.

And if you are not so fortunate as to live in the country or by the sea, you can get lots of fun looking for strange things on the streets or in the parks. There are hundreds of curious-looking people about, you know, and all manner of strange dresses. Then there are queer dogs and cats—dogs with long bodies and short legs, cats of strange colors—new type of cars, unusual advertisements, and all sorts of things.

If you want to have a real exciting competition sometime, get your friend to go for a walk with you in search of curiosities. Take a notebook each and make a list of all the curious things you see, everything that you feel is out of the ordinary. Of course, don't put your little friend's name at the head of your list. And don't compare your lists till you get back home. Then the one who has the longest list of *real* curiosities will have won the game.

The only difficulty you may find will be in deciding whether what you have put down is really truly a curiosity. If you two don't agree, at least be sure you don't quarrel about it. The best way is to let your friend have the benefit of the doubt. It will make him happy even though you feel bad at losing the game yourself.

As you grow up, if you always keep your eyes open, you will see all sorts of curious things, and life will be so much more interesting than if you go along with your eyes shut.

Look at the elephant on the opposite page. There is a curiosity for you! Have you ever seen an elephant having his toenails cut? I don't suppose you have. To be quite exact, this elephant's toenails are really being filed down, not cut. I fancy he looks far happier about it than you do on bath night when Mother gets busy with the scissors!

Now look at that great fir tree growing out of a roof! Isn't that one of the strangest things you ever saw? If you should ever pass through the village of Kilmersdon in Somersetshire, England, you will see the tree itself—that is, if it hasn't been blown down by then. By the way, the roots of this tree do not reach the ground, so it must draw all its life and food out of the roof itself.

When you visit Arizona you must see the famous petrified forest. Here you will find hundreds of fallen trees that were once tall pines and cedars but which have now turned to stone. Through the action of water hundreds of years ago, minerals have taken the place of the wood. And such colors! Many of the stones the Bible describes as part of the walls of the New Jerusalem are to be found here—jasper, amethyst, onyx, and others. Thousands of tons of this beautiful petrified wood have been polished and made into useful ornaments.

In New Mexico there is a great rock standing alone in the midst of a flat desert. It looks so like a ship on the sea that it is known as Ship Rock. In Arizona there is another strange rock with a huge hole in it, like a window. It is called the Window Rock.

Water does many strange things to the earth, especially in forming underground caves and decorating them with beautiful crystals that make all sorts of curious formations. One of the most famous of these is the Mammoth Cave in Kentucky. It was discovered many years ago when a hunter chased a bear into a small opening in the side of a mountain.

In California, where the giant redwood trees grow, there is one tree so large that it has a house inside its trunk. It is called the Tree House. The heart of this tree was burned out many years ago, and now someone has built a store inside it, where he sells souvenirs. The ceiling is fifty feet high. You can get some idea of the size of the tree by comparing it with the lady standing in front of the door.

Another California redwood tree is so large that someone has cut a hole through it large enough for cars to drive through. Just think of driving a car through a tree!

In New Hampshire there is a very curious formation of rocks on a high cliff in the White Mountains. When you look at these rocks from the right position they resemble a human face—the Great Stone Face some call it; others say it is the Old Man of the Mountain. The forehead is a hundred feet high, with nose, lips, and chin in proportion. You can imagine what a giant it appears to be.

Well, this gives you a good start for your new game, doesn't it? Now keep your eyes open, and see how many curiosities you can find yourself.

# Sylvia's Struggle

*I*F THERE WAS ONE thing more than another that Sylvia disliked, it was practicing on the piano.

She more than disliked it—she hated it.

At the moment she was in the front room sitting on the piano stool, trying to make her fingers do what the dots on the piece of paper in front of her told them to do.

Tum-tum-tum, thumped Sylvia. Tum-a-tum-tum-tum.

"Oh dear!" she cried, exasperated. "I can't get the horrid thing right."

Tum-a-tum-a-tum-tum-tum.

"Oh!"

Bang! Sylvia slammed down the lid of the piano.

"I'll never, never practice again," she cried, jumping off the piano stool and running toward the door.

Unfortunately, as she did so, the door opened and in walked Mamma.

"Hello, Sylvia. You haven't learned that piece yet, dear, have you?" asked Mamma.

"No, and I'm not going to," said Sylvia. "I hate practicing; I hate the old piece; I hate the old piano."

"Sylvia, my dear!" exclaimed Mamma. "This won't do. You mustn't give up as easily as that. You'll never get anywhere in life without a struggle. If at first you don't succeed, you must try again."

"I don't want to try again," said Sylvia, pouting.

"Well, let Mamma see what she can do with the piece."

So Mamma sat down at the piano and tried the piece over. It went so easily, and sounded so very pretty, that Sylvia's frown gradually disappeared.

"It's easy for you," she said, "but I shall never be able to play like that."

"Of course you will, darling," said Mamma. "You'll

soon be playing this piece better than I can. Anyhow, teacher wants you to play at the school concert at Christmas."

"Me!" exclaimed Sylvia. "Me play at the school concert? Ha! ha! Wouldn't they all laugh!"

"I don't see why you shouldn't," said Mamma. "There will be other little girls there playing pieces like this, and there's no reason at all why you should let them beat you. All you need is to keep on practicing."

"Practicing!" exclaimed Sylvia. "Practicing! How I hate the very word."

"But you mustn't," said Mamma. "It only means learning by doing something over and over again."

"Over and over again," repeated Sylvia. "That's the worst of it. And somehow it never comes the same twice."

"Well, come along and try again now."

Reluctantly Sylvia went back to the piano and started once more while Mamma went back to her work.

Tum-tum-tum. Tum-a-tum-tum-tum-tum—

"Oh! It's no good. I can't get it right," she cried, bursting into tears.

She felt she simply couldn't start again, and went over to the sofa to cry it out.

Perhaps she was overtired, I don't know, but soon she was fast asleep. The very next thing she heard was

her name being called from the platform at school. The hall seemed to be full of girls all dressed in their best. Sylvia guessed that it must be the Christmas concert.

"Sylvia Silverton," teacher was saying, "will now play for us a delightful little sonata in D minor."

Sylvia started. Was she to play? Evidently. She looked at her dress. Yes, she had on a very beautiful frock which all the girls would admire. It would be very nice, too, going up in front of them all onto the platform. As to the piece, well, she would do her best; and it would be lovely to hear everybody clapping. Perhaps they would want her to come up on the platform again, after she had finished, to play another piece.

And now they *were* clapping. Sylvia flushed, and

267

felt very happy as she walked up the aisle past all her friends, to the platform. Still smiling and blushing, she sat down at the piano and looked at the piece.

Horrors! It was the very piece she had hated practicing. How she wished she had learned it properly. If only she had practiced faithfully. Oh dear! But there was no turning back now. She simply had to go on and hope for the best. Perhaps the girls wouldn't notice the mistakes.

Tum-tum-tum.    Tum-a-tum-a-tum-tum-tum-tum.

"He-he-he!" came from the back of the hall.

"Ssh!" whispered the mistress.

Tum-tum-tum.

"He-he-he-he!" laughed somebody out loud.

"Hoo-hoo-hoo-hoo!" chortled another girl, trying hard to keep it in.

It was too much for Sylvia. In her dream she slammed down the piano lid and ran from the platform.

Bang!

"Whatever is the matter?" cried Mamma, running into the room. "Why, my dear, you've knocked the flowerpot off the window sill. Sylvia!"

"Er—er, where am I?" said Sylvia. "I thought I was at school playing at the concert."

"I wish you had been playing the piano," said Mamma, stooping to pick up the flowerpot.

"I think I shall practice after this, Mamma," said Sylvia, sighing. "It was simply dreadful. I went onto the platform and found I couldn't play at all. I'll try again, Mamma. I really will."

She did; and the concert was a great success.

RUSSELL HARLAN, ARTIST

**Daddy Went to Find Out What Was the Matter With George. He Found Him on the Floor With a Pile of String Around Him in a Hopeless Tangle**

# The Tale of a Tangle

*I*T WAS HOLIDAY TIME,
and George wanted a kite.

It was not the only thing George wanted, by any means, but just for the moment it was the thing he wanted most.

"Dad," he said, "do come and look at the lovely kite they've got in the corner store. It's just the one I want."

"I believe it," said Dad, not much interested.

"Do come and look at it," begged George.

"I've seen lots of kites," said Dad.

"But this is a new kind," persisted George, "and I really must have it. And if we don't go soon, it may be gone."

"Oh, don't be so impatient," replied Dad. "There's no great hurry."

"But there is, really. You see, someone will buy it if we don't. I saw a boy looking in the shop just now, and I'm sure he wanted it."

"Let him have it," said Dad.

"Oh, no, I couldn't," said George, getting desperate. "And after all, Dad, it's only a dime."

Dad pricked up his ears.

"Only ten cents? And who is going to pay for it?"

"Oh, I am, of course. That is—er—if you will lend me the dime."

"Ah!" said Dad, "I seem to have heard that before."

George returned to the attack. He said that he had never had a kite in all his life, that other boys always had kites. Some had two or three. If he had a kite he would be supremely happy.

He would never worry anyone again. Dad would be free to read his paper without any interruption. Dad would not be asked to fly the kite or wind in the string, unless he really wanted to do it. The kite would indeed become the greatest boon to the whole family that had ever been purchased. And all for ten cents, to be paid back, under solemn promise, during the next twelve months.

Either suddenly convinced of George's good intentions or in utter desperation, Dad at last gave in and found himself being escorted to the corner store.

"That's it, that's the one!" cried George. "It's still there. How fortunate that no one bought it while you were making up your mind, Dad."

"What a pity, you mean! By the way, it's rather small and very flimsy."

"Yes," admitted George. "A large one would really be better, but it would cost more money, you know."

"Yes, I see."

They discussed kites for twenty minutes with the lady in the store, and at the conclusion Dad found himself the poorer by fifty cents.

They had decided to take a larger kite, and the ten-cent one was put back in the window.

George was frantic with delight.

"I'll pay you back," he said reassuringly.

"Yes, of course," said Dad, having a vision of the debt being spread over two years instead of one.

They were just leaving the store when Dad noticed something.

"Where is your string?" he said.

"String?" repeated George in dismay.

"Yes, string," said Dad with emphasis. "Got any?"

"Why—er—no," said George ruefully, "I can't say I have. I really never thought about it. Don't they give us the string with the kite?"

"Not usually. The string will cost you another twenty-five cents."

4-18

George's face fell. "I'm afraid I shall have to borrow that as well," he said.

Dad laughed. "I'll give you that too, son. But mind, whatever you do, don't undo that ball of string until you are ready to use it. Then wind it on a thick round piece of wood."

"Oh, I know what to do," said George, "I can do it all right."

They left the store and returned home. Dad had left seventy-five cents there instead of a dime.

At dinnertime there was no sign of George.

"George!" called Dad. "Where are you?"

Mother came in.

"It's all right," she said, "George is having a little trouble, but he'll be along soon."

But George did not come along soon. Dad went to find out what was the matter. He found him in the other room with the ball of string on the floor. To be more correct, it was a *pile* of string. Indeed, it was one appalling, heartbreaking tangle. Poor George sat on the floor beside it, picking, pulling, twisting, winding, his face meanwhile the very picture of gloom.

"What does this mean?" asked Dad. "Is that the lovely ball of string we bought this morning?"

George turned his tear-filled eyes upward and looked into his father's face. Then without saying a word he returned to his seemingly unending task.

"George, how did this happen? Did you undo the ball before you were ready to wind it on the stick?"

George nodded, and the nod threw a tear out on the floor.

"Well," said Dad, "that was deliberate disobedience. You are a most impatient boy, and you deserve to be punished."

"I am," said George.

As for the tangle, well, Mother had a go at it, auntie had a go at it, sister had a go at it, and, of course, Dad had a go at it; and it was not until two days later that Dad's fifty cents soared into the air at the end of that ball of string.

And now every time George sees a kite in the sky he remembers his mistakes and his impatience and determines to be a better boy.

# Little Princess

MAGGIE! MAGGIE!" IT was Mother calling, and she wanted her little daughter to come in to dinner.

But there was no response.

"Maggie! Maggie!" Mother called again. "Come along. Everything will be getting cold."

Still there was silence.

"That's a funny thing," Mother said to herself. "I wonder what can have happened to her? I suppose I'd better go and see."

She went, and after some searching at last found Maggie behind the big shed in the garden. She was pushing her doll's buggy to and fro, quite evidently trying to look important.

"Maggie! didn't you hear me calling you?" asked Mother rather sternly.

"I don't think I did," said Maggie, continuing her stately walk. "I may have, but you see——"

"But you see," said Mother, "when I call you to come in to dinner, I expect you to come at once."

"Oh, but you see," said Maggie, with great solemnity, "I'm a princess."

"A princess!" cried Mother, trying not to laugh. "Since when?"

"Oh, since—well, since just now."

"Well, all right, little princess, you come in to dinner when Mother calls."

"Oh, I couldn't," said Maggie, still very solemn. "You see, Mother, princesses do just what they like."

"Do they?" exclaimed Mother. "Do they? Well, I don't think this one is going to. Come along now, and you can play being a princess again after dinner."

Maggie somehow recognized the light in Mother's eye, and decided that, princess or no princess, it might be just as well to go in to dinner at this very moment.

Most unfortunately the dinner was not to Maggie's liking, and she decided that she wasn't going to eat it.

"Now come, come," said Mother. "You'll make yourself ill if you don't eat your food. Why, you've

eaten beans and potatoes and cabbage many times before this, and enjoyed them."

"But I don't want them today, thank you," said Maggie, pushing her plate away with great formality, and a slight toss of her head.

Mother stared.

"Well!" she exclaimed. "What is it now?"

"You see," said Maggie, "I'm a princess now, and if I don't want my food, I don't have to eat it."

"Are you quite well?" asked Mother.

"Yes, I am very well, thank you," said Maggie, tossing her little head again in such a way that Mother couldn't help smiling.

"Tell me, Maggie," she said, "where did you get this funny idea? Who told you about being a princess?"

"It's a secret."

"I know, but you can tell Mother, can't you?"

"You won't tell anybody?"

"Oh, no."

"Well, then, the little girl next door told me. She said that my name Maggie is short for Margaret, and Margaret is a princess, and all Margarets are princesses. So I'm a princess, too, and I don't have to do what I'm told any more, and I can eat what I like and say what I like, and——"

"Maggie darling!" exclaimed Mother. "What strange ideas little girls get into their tiny heads sometimes. Do you really suppose princesses always do just what they like?"

"Don't they?" asked Maggie a little anxiously. "That's what the little girl next door said."

"But what does she know about it?" replied Mother. "Why, princesses, especially when they are little girls, have to mind what they do more than anybody else. When Princess Margaret was your age she had the strictest program to follow every day. She was called at seven o'clock by her nurse——"

"And did she get up at once?"

"Of course she did," said Mother, "as all good little girls should do. Then she had breakfast, went for a walk, and then settled down to her lessons."

"Do princesses have to do lessons?"

"They have to study very hard," said Mother. "And while Princess Margaret did not go to school, she had governesses who saw to it that she learned what she was taught. Lessons went on most of the morning, and then she had

lunch at one o'clock. She was not allowed to say that she didn't like her food. Oh, no, indeed! After lunch she went for another walk, and then returned to more lessons until four o'clock. After that came supper, and a very early bedtime."

"So she really couldn't do just what she liked?" asked Maggie, evidently disappointed.

"Oh, dear, no," said Mother. "That wouldn't have been good for her. You see, the king and queen wanted her to grow up to be a fine, lovely, well-mannered lady; and if she had been allowed to be a rude, naughty, disobedient little girl, she would have grown up that way, and then nobody would have liked her."

There was a moment's silence.

"Mamma," said Maggie, with a little puzzled look

on her face, "are you quite sure? Do all princesses have to be so very, very good?"

"I think so," said Mother.

"Then I think," said Maggie, "that I'll just be an ordinary little girl, after all."

# Saved by an Onion

*J*N THE EARLY days of American history, when the Western States were being developed, some of the hardest-working people were ministers of the gospel. These were the circuit riders, who rode on horseback from one community to another, preaching and conducting baptisms, marriages, and funerals. Sometimes they would be away from home for months at a time, enduring all sorts of hardships and riding thousands of miles a year.

Mr. Matthews was one of these brave and busy circuit riders. He had a huge parish, covering hundreds of miles in every direction, which constantly called for all his time and attention. What with these heavy duties and his large family of twelve children, he was sometimes a very tired and harassed man.

Coming home one day after a long absence, he found that his son Jack had failed to complete some work that had been assigned him. Heated words were

281

spoken, and it was not long before Jack was suffering from the effects of a severe thrashing. Father simply would not put up with disobedience.

Now Jack was a high-spirited boy, and nothing wounded his pride so much as being thrashed, especially when he felt that he did not deserve it. This time he was so angry that he determined to run away.

His favorite sister, Margaret, who was about his own age, pleaded with him not to go, but he would not listen to her. She begged him to think over his rash resolve, to let everything rest for a few days, but nothing moved him. He was fully determined to go.

Next morning, without saying good-by to anyone but Margaret, Jack went away, determined never to return to his Father's house.

Now it was Margaret's turn to be cross. She, of course, sided with Jack, and said it was her Father's fault that he had gone away. Therefore she would have nothing to do with her Father, or with his religion.

Every day she became more and more bitter. She would hardly speak to either of her parents and positively refused to take any part in family worship. She would neither read the Bible nor say her prayers, and in her heart she secretly resolved that she would never be a Christian, never!

Meanwhile no word came back from Jack. He had vanished completely out of the home. Margaret felt that the joy of life had gone away with him, and her heart became hard as steel.

Then one morning, while preparing the dinner, Mother discovered that she needed just one more onion, and Margaret was the only daughter near at hand to send.

"Margaret!" called Mother. "I do so need just one more onion to finish this potpie. I wish you would go and get me one."

"Where are they?" asked Margaret coldly.

"In the barn, on the second floor," said Mother. "Mind how you go up the ladder, dear. And you might as well bring me two or three extra ones while you are about it."

Margaret went without a word, or even a smile. She had long since ceased to smile around the house, and was secretly longing for the day when she, too, could run away. Then she would go and find Jack.

Going over to the barn, she climbed the ladder to the second floor, and, looking around, soon saw where the onions had been laid out for winter use. She picked

up half a dozen, and was walking back to the ladder, when she heard a noise below.

Footsteps! Someone was coming stealthily toward the ladder.

Who could it be?

Holding her breath, she listened and guessed that it must be her Father, the very last person on earth she wished to meet just then.

Suddenly all the hatred she had been fostering in her heart overflowed. She did not want to speak to him, no, nor to look at him. She never would again, never!

But what could she do?

Looking around quickly, she spied an old, unused door leaning against the wall. It was the only possible shelter; so on tiptoe she ran swiftly toward it, and was barely hidden when she heard her Father coming up the last section of the ladder.

Holding her breath for fear he would detect her

presence, she waited anxiously, hoping he would go down again immediately when he found the loft empty.

But he did not go down. Instead Margaret heard a strange sound as of something falling gently on the floor, and she held her hands together in fright.

After a few moments of fearful suspense she heard her Father talking out loud. Had two people come up into the loft?

No. He was praying!

Cramped behind that door, Margaret listened to the most wonderful prayer she had ever heard—and she couldn't run away from it. She just had to stay and hear every word.

Father was praying for his family. For every child,

from the oldest to the youngest, for Margaret herself, and especially for Jack. When he reached Jack he broke down completely, sobbing as if his heart would break; asking God to forgive him for being so angry with Jack as to drive him away from home; praying that even now God would move upon Jack's heart by His Holy Spirit and bring him back again.

Margaret was stunned, overwhelmed.

So Father did love Jack after all! And wanted him home again! And was so very, very sorry he had been angry with him!

More than that, he was willing to pray for Margaret, too! Margaret, who had been so rude to him, so heartlessly cruel to him all these many weeks since Jack had left. She knew she had not prayed for Father like that.

Suddenly she felt she could not stand it a moment longer. She must run from the scene, or her heart would break.

Margaret rose and slipped from behind the door. As she did so, she caught sight of Father kneeling on the floor, wiping the tears from his eyes.

She gave in.

"Father, I'm sorry," she said, putting her arms around his neck and bursting into tears.

"So are we all, Margaret," he said. And everything was all right again from that moment.

Meanwhile, Mother was beginning to fuss about the missing onion, wondering why Margaret had been so long getting it. But when she saw Father and daughter coming across the yard with arms around each other, faces tear-stained but radiant, with a Mother's intuition she suddenly understood, and ran out to meet them, the onion and the pie all forgotten.

That night, believe it or not, Jack returned.

(In later years, by the way, Jack himself became a minister, and Margaret a minister's wife.)

# When Daddy Phoned

*M*ASTER JOHN WAS THE idol of his Daddy's heart. Everything that Master John did was perfectly all right—to Daddy.

Mamma would sometimes tell Daddy at nighttime about some of the mischief Master John had been up to during the day. But Daddy would say, without the least sympathy for Mamma, "Poor little dear, he had to amuse himself somehow, didn't he?"

Even when Master John had wiped his coal-black fingers all over Mamma's newly washed clothes, all that Daddy said was, "Ah, but he's a bright boy; he must have known those clothes were clean, or he wouldn't have done it."

But one day Daddy had a little experience with Master John himself.

He was in the city, and in a terrible hurry to get an important document which he thought he had left at home. In a frenzy of anxiety lest he might have lost it on the train, he rushed to the nearest telephone and tried to call Mamma.

And this is what happened next:

"Is that Henford 4242?"

"Yaaaaaaaa."

"I say, is that Henford 4242?"

"Heeeeeeee."

"There's something wrong with the phone. Is that you, Maggie?"

"Dad-dad-dad-dad-dad-dad."

"What is the matter? I want that document I left on the hall table this morning."

"Goo-goo-goo-goo-goo-goo."

"Can't you understand what I say? I've lost that document. At least I haven't got it. Is it at home? Can't you hear me? Is that Henford 4242?"

"Dad-dad-dad-dad-dad-dad."

Daddy hung up with a scowl of impatience.

When he reached home that night he asked for an

explanation. He could not afford to waste good money like that on telephone calls. And when he did call, why did not someone answer him in an intelligent way? Whoever dared to say all that gibberish when he was anxiously awaiting news of an important document? And so on.

Mamma waited until it was all over. Then she burst into peals of laughter.

"I came in just as you hung up," she said at last, "and what did I find but Master John trying to talk into the phone with the earpiece held up as if he had used it for years."

"Well!" exclaimed Daddy. "So it was Master John, was it? A remarkable boy, my dear. I always did say he was a most intelligent child. I must go up and kiss him for that right now, even if he is asleep."

"Well, of all things!" said Mamma, as Daddy bounded eagerly upstairs.

# Old Joe's Surprise

*J*N THOSE BAD OLD days when slavery was still practiced, Old Joe stood in the market place awaiting the auction.

He was a grand specimen of manhood, big, strong, and healthy, but on his face at this moment there was an expression of anger and stubbornness that only faintly reflected the rebellious feelings in his heart.

His master had died, and in consequence he and many others of his fellow slaves were to be sold at public auction to the highest bidder. How he hated it all! He hated his chains; he hated the system which made it possible for human beings to be bought and sold like cattle; he hated the dreadful humiliation.

While he stood there waiting in the hot sun, there grew up in his heart a determination that he would not be bought, and if he were, he would never work for his new master.

Presently his name was called. The auctioneer began to describe him. "Joe. Fine strong fellow. Lots of hard work in him yet——"

"I will not work!" cried Joe in desperation.

291

The auctioneer ignored him, and went on giving his age, his height, his weight, and other particulars. "What offers?" he concluded.

Someone made a bid. "I will not work!" cried Joe at the top of his voice.

No one bothered. The bidding went on.

Joe listened with interest that merged into amazement. He had no idea he was worth so much. Up and up went the price. Gradually the number of bidders decreased, but two or three went on. One man seemed determined to purchase him whatever the cost might be.

At last, when the price had reached the highest figure Joe had ever heard offered for a slave, the hammer fell. He was sold!

Soon his new master came over to where he was standing.

"I will not work," said Joe. "You can thrash me, but I will not work. I told you that before."

292

The new master said nothing, but proceeded to lead him away to his wagon. All the way out to the plantation Joe kept on muttering to himself, "I won't work. I won't work."

At last they arrived, and the master, instead of taking Joe to the usual dirty slave quarters, led him to a neat little cottage, remarking, "Joe, this will be your home while you are with us."

"This for me?" said Joe, surprised. "Thank you, but I will not work."

"You do not need to work," said his master. "Just live here as long as you please."

"But, master," cried Joe in utter amazement, "aren't you going to try to make me work?"

"Oh, no," said the master quietly. "I bought you to set you free."

"To set me free! Oh, master," cried Joe, falling on

his knees before him, "how can I thank you enough? I will gladly serve you always and do anything you want me to do."

From that moment Joe became the most faithful and loyal servant his master ever had.

And children, what that good master did for Joe, Jesus has done for us. He saw us standing in the market place, as it were, chained with sin, and our hearts full of rebellion, and He gave everything He had to set us free. The Bible says that we were redeemed not "with corruptible things, as silver and gold; . . . but with the precious blood of Christ." 1 Peter 1:18, 19.

When such a price has been paid for us, what should we do? What should we say to Him who paid it? What else can we say than, "Jesus, dear Master, we will love and serve Thee all our days"?

294

# Filling the Coal Scuttle

*F*ATHER WAS READING the newspaper, Mother was knitting, and Tim and Tiny were sitting at the table doing their homework.

"It seems to be getting colder," said Father, looking up. "Let's have some more coal on the fire, Tim."

Tim jumped up and went over to the coal scuttle.

"It's empty," he said, turning to go back to his homework.

"Well, we've got to have some coal," said Father, "or the fire will go out. Better fill it."

"It's Tiny's turn to fill it."

Tiny looked up from his books.

"What's that?" he asked. "My turn? Oh, no. It's Tim's turn. I'm sure it is."

"No, it isn't," said Tim. "I know it's Tiny's turn to fill it. I filled it last time, and I'm not going to fill it again now."

"But we've got to have coal," said Father. "Get it filled."

"It's Tiny's turn," said Tim with determination.

"No, it isn't," said Tiny emphatically. "And anyway, I washed the dishes this evening, and he only dried them; so he ought to fill the old thing."

"No, I should not," retorted Tim. "And if you're going to talk about dishes, I washed the dinner things, so there."

"And I washed the breakfast things yesterday, so————"

"But what about the coal?" asked Father. "I'm waiting for the coal. When is it coming?"

"It's Tiny's turn," stated Tim again.

"Now look here," said Father, "that's enough. Both of you go outside the door for two minutes, and decide who is going to get it. But don't come back without it. Hurry up, or the fire will be out."

Scowling at each other, the two boys made for the door. As it closed, Father could hear a high-pitched conversation going on.

"It's your turn."

"It is not, I tell you, it's yours."

"Well, I'm not going to fetch it. You should."

"No, I shouldn't. It's your job."

"It's yours."

"It isn't mine. It's yours. You've got to get it."

296

Gradually the voices grew fainter as they moved away toward the coal shed.

"I wonder what is happening out there," said Father to Mother. "I suppose I shall have to go and see about it, after all."

"I wouldn't," said Mother. "Let's wait and see what they do."

They did not have long to wait. Suddenly there was a loud bang on the door, and two beaming faces burst into the living room.

"Here's the coal," said Tim.

"Just in time," cried Tiny.

"Well, that's fine," cried Father. "You both look happy. How did you fix it up?"

"Fix what up?" asked Tim. "Oh, yes. Why, we got a great idea. Tim filled half of it, and I filled the other half. So here we are."

"Splendid!" cried Father.

"That was a good idea," said Mother.

"I don't know why we didn't think of it before," said Tiny.

"Neither do I," said Father, smiling. "But it just

shows that when there's a job to be done, it is a thousand times better for people to work together than to waste time arguing whose job it really is."

"It reminds me," said Mother, "of that little rhyme which says:

> " 'Let's all pull together
> In all kinds of weather,
> And see what we can do.' "

"It's always a fine thing to pull together," said Father with a laugh; "and as for the weather, it's warming up nicely now we've got that coal!"

At which two heads bent over their books once more, and the fire played up again on the hearth.

# Joan's Jewels

$M$OTHER, I WISH I could have some jewelry to wear," said Joan one day.

"Jewelry!" exclaimed Mother in alarm. "What has put that strange idea into your little head?"

"Oh, well, Mother," said Joan, "it looks so pretty. All the other girls wear it, and I feel so odd and plain."

"What are they wearing nowadays that looks so attractive?" asked Mother.

"Gold bracelets and necklaces and things. And some have rings with diamonds and pearls in them."

"Real ones?"

"Oh, no, not real ones," said Joan. "They couldn't afford to buy real ones."

"And you really think those trinkets are pretty?"

"Oh, yes, ever so pretty," said Joan. "And one day I'm going to buy some for my very own."

"I wouldn't," said Mother, "if I were you. It would be a waste of money. No girl needs to wear a collection of cheap bangles to make herself look beautiful. In fact, I think it really makes her look cheap."

But Joan was not satisfied. In her little heart she

yearned to have some jewelry "like the other girls." At last she felt she couldn't wait any longer; so she decided to go and buy some for herself.

Without telling Mother, she slipped out of the house one day, carrying her purse with all her savings in it, and wended her way down to the stores.

It was not long before she came to one that had a display of jewelry in the window. And how cheap it was! Why, there were beautiful gold necklaces for a quarter each, gold bracelets for ten cents, a diamond ring for thirty-five cents, and a gorgeous pearl necklace for forty-nine cents!

Joan felt like an explorer suddenly discovering hidden treasures. This was just what she had been wanting so long, and now she could have everything she had set her heart upon. So, clutching her purse tightly, she entered the shop.

Never had she so enjoyed spending money, though now and then she had a peculiar feeling somewhere inside that perhaps Mother wouldn't be pleased.

She bought two of the necklaces and four of the bracelets, so that she could have two on each wrist. Then two gold rings, at ten cents each. Several times she picked up the diamond ring, but she hesitated to spend so much. Thirty-five cents would use up all the money she had left, and it had taken a long time to save so much.

At last, however, the temptation became too strong for her. So the diamond ring was bought, and Joan sallied forth with all the jewelry fully displayed upon her person—and just one little penny left in her purse.

How she strutted along the street, as proud of her little self as any peacock in a king's garden! Passing some of her girl friends, she drew herself up to her full height and looked at them as if to say, "Humph! I'm just as pretty as you are now."

The girls smiled at her. Some of them laughed, but Joan didn't like that, and thought they must be jealous.

As she turned into her own street, her heart suddenly seemed to stop beating for a moment. She felt cold and shivery all over. What would Mother say if she went indoors like this?

Well, anyway, thought Joan, Mother would have to see it sometime, so why not now? Better get it over with. Maybe she would like it and would say how it suited her.

She opened the door and went in. Mother was ironing in the kitchen. She looked up and gave Joan a cheery smile.

"Been to town?" she asked.

"Yes," said Joan rather sheepishly.

"Lovely day for a walk," said Mother.

"Yes," said Joan.

"Going to help me iron?"

"If you like."

So Joan helped with the ironing, then with the supper, then with the dishes, while the bracelets and necklaces clanked about her; but never a word did Mother say about the jewelry. Joan began to wonder whether Mother had noticed it; yet she must have.

Somehow Joan didn't like this silence, this apparent total lack of interest in what she had done; yet she dared not mention it herself, for fear Mother would express her disapproval.

Several days went by; but never a word did Mother say about the jewelry, much though she loathed the sight of it.

Pretty soon the jewelry began to speak for itself. The pearl necklace was first. The string broke and let several of the pearls go down the kitchen drain.

Joan was very much upset, but she kept her feelings to herself, not wanting to tell Mother anything about it.

Then the bracelets began to dull, and one day Mother—out of the corner of one eye—noticed that Joan was busy with a polishing cloth trying to bring back their once brilliant color. But the more she rubbed, the blacker the bracelets became. By the look on Joan's face, Mother guessed that it was nearly time to say something.

That night, before Joan went to bed, Mother read a few verses from the Bible, where it says: "In like manner also, that women adorn themselves in modest apparel; . . . not with . . . gold, or pearls, or costly array; but (which becometh women professing godliness) with good works." 1 Timothy 2:9, 10.

Then she turned over the page and read again: "Whose adorning let it not be that outward adorning of . . . wearing of gold, or of putting on of apparel; but let it be the hidden man of the heart, in that which is not corruptible, even the ornament of a meek and quiet spirit, which is in the sight of God of great price." 1 Peter 3:3, 4.

"I don't know," said Mother, "whether you know

what the expression 'not corruptible' means, but it suggests something that will not wear out or get tarnished; something that doesn't forever need polishing to keep it bright."

Joan looked very thoughtful, and her eyes looked down upon her tawdry, blackened little gold bracelets.

"After all," said Mother, looking far away out of the window, "nobody who loves Jesus, nobody who has become the dwelling place of His Holy Spirit, needs to try to make herself beautiful with 'costly array.' Jesus Himself makes people beautiful, in word, in deed, and in character. And somehow His beauty shines out of their faces and makes all other ornaments unnecessary. One doesn't need to gild the lily, or paint the rose, you know."

Joan sat still awhile; then she kissed Mother good night and went to bed.

Next morning she came downstairs minus her jewelry.

And nobody, except Joan herself, knows what happened to it, for she never wore it any more.

# Giving and Getting

$\mathcal{T}$HAT STORY ABOUT Joan and her jewels reminds me of another little girl who decided that she wished to go shopping on her own.

We will call this little girl Gwennie, so that you won't know who she really is.

Now Gwennie had been staying for some time with her grandmother, and they had become fast friends. In fact, both of them felt very sorry that the day of parting was drawing nearer and nearer, when Gwennie would have to go back to her Mother and Father again.

One afternoon Gwennie was a bit restless, and she begged grandma to take her out in the car. Grandma was not feeling like a ride just then, and made some excuse that she couldn't go. Gwennie looked sad, and grandma felt sorry that she had said no.

A few moments later grandma called Gwennie to her.

"I have an idea," she said. "How would you like to go shopping all on your own? You know, just to buy something nice for yourself."

306

"Oh, I'd love it!" exclaimed Gwennie. "I've always wanted to go by myself. But I haven't any money."

"That's all right," said grandma. "I'll give you a quarter, and you can get anything that you think will make you happy."

"And may I go into Woolworth's?"

"Yes, if you want to."

"Oh, goody, goody!" exclaimed Gwennie, as though the greatest ambition of her little life had at last been satisfied.

Soon she was dressed and on her way to town. How perfectly lovely it was to be going all alone, and with a whole quarter in her purse to spend for anything she wished!

At last she neared the stores and was soon looking

in the windows. Arriving at the big red store with the
gold letters on it, she went inside.

What millions and millions of wonderful things!
Gwennie thought to herself, as she wandered up and
down the aisles almost in a dream.

What should she buy? How difficult it was to decide! She wanted everything she saw, but of course a
quarter wouldn't go very far.

Well, should it be a doll? There were some beautiful dolls, dressed dolls and baby dolls. But she had
plenty of dolls.

A new purse, or handbag? A box of paints, or some
pretty handkerchiefs?

Then she noticed a very lovely flowering plant in a
pot, all for fifteen cents.

"Grandma would love that," she thought, as she
stood looking at it, wondering if she should spend
such a lot of money all at once.

"It would make grandma very happy; I'm sure it would," she said to herself. And then, with a thrill of joy she had never known before, she paid the money and took the plant.

So much happiness did she feel that she began to wonder if she shouldn't spend what she had left on something else for grandma, and after a lot of looking, she exchanged her remaining ten cents for—of all things—a flour shaker! "I'm sure she will find it very useful," Gwennie told herself.

Soon she was on the way home again, hugging her two precious parcels, and so happy that she felt as if she were walking on air.

Into the house she bounded, her face radiant.

"Look what I've brought you," she cried, as grandma came to meet her.

"For me?" cried grandma. "But I sent you to buy something for yourself."

"I know," said Gwennie, "but you'll love these things, and I'm so happy."

"So happy?" said grandma, taking the two little parcels out of Gwennie's trembling hands, while tears started from her eyes. "Why so happy, darling?"

"Oh, grandma," cried Gwennie. "I was just thinking on the way home how much happier it makes us to give than to receive. Giving is *so* much lovelier than getting. Don't you think so?"

"It always is," said grandma, taking Gwennie in her arms. "Always."

# He Wanted Love

*C*HARLIE'S HOME WAS a single room in one of the worst slums of a certain big city. In that room lived his stepfather, his Mother, and his brother and sisters. Brought up in such a place, Charlie was a typical little slum child, dirty, untidy, slovenly, and mischievous.

He had nowhere to play but in the streets and the river, and nobody to play with except other slum children like himself.

He was sure nobody loved him, for his stepfather was always brutal, and his Mother coarse, and both of them drank liquor.

Some of the other boys with whom he played would be invited now and then by some church or welfare society to go on a picnic, but always he was left out. "Too dirty," he would hear someone say. "I don't like his face, either," another would chime in. "He can't be a good boy."

Then one day he heard something different. Someone spoke up for him.

"I think this boy should go," a woman was saying

as she pointed at poor, ragged Charlie. "Let's take him."

"Oh, no, not he; we never take him," replied another.

"All the more reason why he should go now," said the first woman. "He needs the outing more than all the others. In fact, I insist that he go."

"Very well, then. Anything to please you, madam. Charlie, you will be included this time. Make yourself as clean as you can, and be sure to be at the meeting place promptly."

Something surged through Charlie's little heart which he had not known before. Somebody wanted him! Somebody insisted that he go!

He would be there on time. Oh, yes, indeed, and as clean as he could be. Perhaps that pleasant woman would be there, too.

At last the great day arrived, and early in the morning several busloads of happy youngsters waved farewell to the slums and turned their faces toward the open country and joy unbounded.

The picnic grounds were beautifully situated

beside a wide, swiftly flowing river. The children had never seen anything quite so wonderful. Some thought it must be heaven.

In a sheltered portion of the river bathing was permitted, and soon the boys were having a great time in the water.

All of a sudden the peace and happiness of the picnic was interrupted by a piercing shriek. A boy called Peter had foolishly climbed over the protecting rope and was out in the rushing stream.

Pandemonium reigned as everybody rushed to the riverbank to see Peter go by. He was certain to be drowned, they all said, for no one would attempt to swim out to him in a dangerous river like that.

Then, like a flash, somebody dived from the top of the bank.

There was a gasp. Who could it be? All they could see was a small tousled head bobbing in the water and

two strong arms striking out toward the drowning boy.

It was Charlie, who had learned to swim like a fish in the muddy water of the river near his home.

On and on he swam, getting nearer and nearer to the boy, grabbing him at last and fighting his way back to the bank.

Scores of people were waiting when they came ashore, and they crowded around Peter's prostrate form.

"Is he dead?" they asked. "Will he come around? Fetch blankets and hot-water bottles. Try first aid on him."

Everything possible was done, and soon Peter was sitting up, dazed but smiling, wrapped in blankets, drinking hot chocolate, and being fussed over generally.

Suddenly a woman called out, "But where's the other boy—the one who saved him?" It was the kind woman who had said Charlie must go to the picnic.

Nobody knew. She left the crowd and went to look for him. Charlie was standing some distance away, shivering in his wet clothes.

Running back to the crowd, she said, "Let's take up a collection for the boy who rescued Peter. That's the least we can do."

Everybody agreed, and soon someone was going around with a hat. Everyone had a part and there was quite a sum of money in it when at last it was handed to the woman. She hurried back to Charlie.

"Here you are," she said. "They all wanted to show you how grateful they are that you saved Peter's life."

"No, thanks," said Charlie. "I don't want money."

The woman was astonished. "Then what——?" she began.

Charlie looked over to where Peter was sitting, warm and comfortable now, with people all around him.

"I just want a bit of love like that other boy's getting," he said.

Somehow the kind woman understood. Tears flooded into her eyes. She had discovered the secret longing of this poor boy's heart. Now she knew all that had been the matter with him. Perhaps, she thought, other poor boys might feel like this, too.

"You shall have it," she said, "and much more."

And she kept her word.

315

# Why Jack Was Late

*J*T WAS A FINE, COLD afternoon, with plenty of snow about, and not too much wind. Just the time for a hike to the lake, thought Jack. Harry and Kenneth agreed.

"You'll be back at five, won't you, Jack," said his Mother, as she bade him good-by. "And mind you, no going on the ice. It isn't safe yet."

"All right, Mother," said Jack, running off to join his friends.

Soon they were out of town, trudging merrily along the highway which led to the lake.

"I wonder how thick the ice is by now," said Kenneth.

"Not more than two inches," answered Jack. "There'll have to be another week of this weather before we dare skate on it."

"Rats," said Kenneth. "I wouldn't be surprised if we could skate on part of it this afternoon."

"Maybe so," said Harry, "but which part? The trouble is you never know where it's going to crack."

"Anyway," said Jack, "we won't have time to try,

because I have to be home at five o'clock. We shall just have time to look it over and hurry back."

"Aw," said Kenneth, "that's no fun. I want to skate, not just walk there and back and do nothing."

"But that's just what we agreed to do before we started," said Jack. "Of course, we can't skate for another week at least."

"We'll see when we get there," said Kenneth.

At last they reached the lakeside. Kenneth hurried forward onto the ice.

"Now, Ken," said Jack, "do be careful. You know it can't hold your weight yet."

"Aw, it's safe enough," said Ken. "Look, it's hard as rock ten feet from shore."

"Maybe it is; but farther out——"

"Oh, come on," called Ken. "It's just wonderful. I'm twenty yards out, and not a sign of a crack."

HERBERT
RUDEEN

"No," called Jack, "I'm not coming. I don't believe it's safe. You are taking big chances. What's more, I promised my Mother——"

"Ha, ha!" laughed Kenneth. "Harry, you come, then."

"No, thanks," said Harry. "I'd rather not. I promised my Mother, too."

"Ha, ha, ha!" Kenneth laughed again. "Mother's little darlings. Oh! It's cracking! Help! Help!"

Sure enough, the ominous sound of cracking ice reached the two boys on the shore.

Kenneth made a leap for safety, but again the ice cracked under him, and in a moment he was floundering in the water.

"Help!" he screamed. "Help! I'm sinking!"

Jack looked at Harry. Now what should they do?

Without a word they ran onto the ice and hurried cautiously toward the spot where Kenneth was grasping frantically at the thin edge of ice around him.

"Get down flat," said Jack to Harry. "I'll go first, and you hold my ankles."

Down they both went, crawling as best they could across the remaining path of thin ice that separated them from Kenneth.

"Give me your hand, Ken," said Jack as he drew near. "And then try your best to scramble out. Harry's holding on to me."

Kenneth, shivering from head to foot, and scared
almost to death, stood at last on the bank. With ice-cold
water dripping from his hair, his clothes, his shoes, he
was a picture of misery.

"You'd better run home," said Harry, "or you'll
catch a death of cold."

"I daren't," Kenneth almost screamed; "I promised
my Mother, too."

"You must," said Jack. "If you stay in those wet
things much longer, you'll get pneumonia."

"I daren't, I tell you!" cried Kenneth, his teeth chat-
tering.

Jack looked at Harry. Then they took off Kenneth's
wet coat and shirt, and between them fixed him up as
best they could with their own clothes. Then, huddling

319

together to keep one another warm, they hurried homeward as fast as they could.

It was long past five now. When Jack didn't come
on time, his Mother was first angry and then worried.
She began to wish she had never let him go to the
lake. There had been so much trouble up there. At
six-fifty she went to the telephone to call the police.
Just then she heard the back door being opened quietly,
and guessed that it was Jack. Worry vanished, and
anger returned.

"You naughty boy," she said in a loud, cross voice.
"You promised me you would be back at five, and it's
nearly seven o'clock. I was just going to call the police.
Don't you ever do this again. Now you can go straight
to bed without any supper."

Jack didn't say a word, hoping against hope that

his Mother wouldn't no-
tice that he was minus his
coat and his scarf. Quickly
he slipped upstairs, and
was soon in bed. He didn't
mind going to bed, but he
did miss his supper. He
was so hungry that he felt
he could eat everything in
the larder. In fact, he was
too hungry to sleep.

About nine-thirty the telephone rang. Jack listened. He heard his Mother talking.

"Ken's Mother, you say? . . . Why, what happened? He did, did he? . . . Oh, but that's wonderful. . . . Jack never said a word. . . . And to think I sent him to bed without any supper! . . . Well, excuse me. I'm so glad Ken's all right, but I must go and see Jack."

A moment later Mother was bounding into Jack's room. Jack was snoring.

"Oh, Jack, Ken's Mother has just told me. It's just marvelous. I'm so proud of you. Jack, Jack, wake up, Jack! Do you hear? I'm so sorry I sent you to bed. I didn't know. You never said. Jack!"

Jack opened one eye, and with half a smile looked up into Mother's eager face.

"What about the supper?" he murmured softly, as though half asleep.

And what a supper it was!

VERNON NYE. ARTIST

**Nora and Brenda Were Having a Thrilling Time Pillow Fighting, Till, Crash!
Brenda Fell Off the Bed. The Noise Alarmed the Mothers Downstairs**

# After Dark

*O*H, NORA!" CRIED
Mother one day as she opened a letter at the breakfast
table. "Isn't this wonderful news? Your Aunt Elizabeth
is coming to stay with us for a whole week, and she's
going to bring Brenda along with her. Won't that be
lovely?"

Nora didn't appear to be very much pleased.

Mother noticed it.

"Why, dear," she said, "aren't you glad Brenda is
coming? It will be so much fun for you to have her to
play with you."

"I don't want Brenda to come," said Nora.

"Oh, my dear, why not?" asked Mother, surprised.
"My little girl isn't feeling a little selfish again, is she?"

Mother, you see, knew a good deal about Nora, and
how, being the only child in the family, she liked to
have everything her own way. In fact, Mother had
really invited Brenda just to help Nora learn the joy
of sharing her playthings happily, and to teach her how
to get along with other people.

"She'll break my best dollies," said Nora, "and

she'll mess up all my toys. I wish she wouldn't come."

"Oh, but Nora," said Mother, "you could have such a wonderful time together if you would give her a friendly welcome and try to be pleasant to her. Then she would be pleasant to you, and both of you would be happy."

"I don't want her to come," repeated Nora. "Anyway, where would she sleep?"

"I thought it would be nice if she slept with you," said Mother. "After all, she is your cousin, and——"

"I won't have her in my bed," snapped Nora, stamping her little foot. "Why, she would take up all the room and I never would be comfortable a single minute. Anyway, she might kick me."

"Oh, but she's not so big as that," smiled Mother. "And after all, dear, you have a very big bed for a little girl. There's plenty of room in it for two."

"No, there isn't!" said Nora. "I don't want anybody in my bed. I don't want anybody in my bedroom. I don't want anybody to touch my things. I don't want anybody——"

"But darling," said Mother, "you shouldn't feel that way. Why, you'll never be happy in life if you just keep all your things to yourself. Try sharing them for once, and see how very, very happy you will be."

"I won't!" cried Nora, pouting. "I won't have anybody in my bed. I won't; so there."

With that, she stormed out of the room and slammed the door.

Mother folded up the letter and finished her breakfast alone, doing a little thinking at the same time.

Three days later Brenda and her Mother arrived. Alas, it was a very cold reception the little girl received from Nora.

"Now, Mother," Nora whispered as the visitors were led upstairs, "remember, I don't want her in my room."

Mother didn't even appear to listen. Opening Nora's bedroom door, she said, "Here you are, Brenda, dear. I know you'll be glad to sleep in here with Nora while you are with us."

"Oh, yes!" cried Brenda, looking around at the spotless room with its pretty yellow curtains, its green carpet, and its beautiful furniture. "This will be just wonderful. I know I shall be very happy here. Thank you so much."

Nora glared, and when Mother passed on to the next bedroom, she said to Brenda, "Well, if you have to stay in my room, you'll have to be very careful of my things. You mustn't touch one of them unless I tell you. So there!"

"I won't; really, I won't," said Brenda. "I shall be so happy just looking at them."

"And mind," said Nora, "when we go to bed tonight, don't you dare take up too much room, or I don't know what I'll do to you. I'm not used to having anyone in my bed."

"Oh, I won't take up too much room," laughed Brenda, wondering whether Nora was really serious about it. "I'll just be as small as a peanut. You'll see."

But Nora *was* serious. She couldn't get reconciled to having anybody in her own precious room, not even Brenda; and Brenda, she had to admit, was rather an interesting little girl, after all.

At last bedtime came, and the two Mothers came in to kiss their little girls good night.

There they lay, as far apart as possible, Brenda at one edge of the bed, Nora at the other.

"I hope you have a lovely, comfortable sleep," said Nora's Mother, "and wake up very happy in the morning."

"I shan't sleep a wink," said Nora.

"I shall," said Brenda; "I'm so cozy in here."

"Well, good night, dears."

"Good night!"

The Mothers went downstairs, smiling at each other and wondering what would happen next.

They did not have long to wait.

"Get over," said Nora. "You touched me with your foot."

"Sorry," said Brenda. "I didn't mean to."

A pause.

"Move over, can't you!" snapped Nora. "You are too near the middle."

"All right." And Brenda moved.

Silence for a while.

"Nora," whispered Brenda.

"Yes. What do you want?"

"Did you ever have a pillow fight?"

"No. Why?"

"It's lots of fun. I've had them with my brother ever so many times."

"What do you do?"

"S-sh! I'll tell you." And Brenda, in awed whispers, told just how it was done.

Nora was interested. She had never had anybody to play a game like this with her.

Pretty soon they were both sitting up in bed; then standing up.

"I'll start," said Brenda.

Wallop! Down came the pillow on Nora's head.

"Ouch!" cried Nora, stepping backward.

"Now you try!" said Brenda.

"I'll try," said Nora as she brought her pillow down on Brenda as hard as she could, almost falling off the bed as she did so.

The fun was on.

Bang! Bang! Bang!

Wallop! Wallop! Wallop!

Crash!

Brenda had fallen onto the floor, but in a moment she was up again and the two were banging away with the pillows, sometimes missing, sometimes hitting, as they staggered all over the springy mattress. And so the fun went merrily on, amid shrieks of suppressed laughter, until they were out of breath.

"There seem to be strange noises upstairs," said Nora's Mother. "I wonder what is happening."

"I wonder," said Brenda's Mother.

Bang! Bang! Bang!

Wallop! Wallop! Wallop!

"Perhaps we had better go and see what they are doing up there."

"Perhaps we had."

They started upstairs.

Suddenly silence fell.

"S-sh!" cried Brenda. "They're coming! Quick, into bed!"

There was a scramble under the sheets.

"Hug me tight!" said Brenda. "And let's pretend we're asleep."

A moment later they were both lying in the middle of the bed, breathing deeply, their eyes tight shut.

"The darlings," said the two Mothers as they looked down at the "sleeping" pair, close in each other's arms.

"I knew they'd be happy together," said Brenda's Mother.

"Er—er—yes," said Nora's Mother, "I hoped they would be."

And they were.

"I like Brenda so much," said Nora one day. "She's such good fun, and we have the most glorious time together. You should have seen her bathing my best dolly today. You would have screamed, Mother; really you would."

"So you're glad that she came, after all?" asked Mother, with a strange smile playing about the corners of her mouth.

"Of course," said Nora, "I always wanted her to come. Really I did!"

And Mother smiled again.

# Frontiers of Peace

*N*OT LONG AGO I WAS driving up the beautiful highway that follows the Pacific Coast all the way from Mexico to Canada, when I came upon a very unusual beautiful archway.

At first it seemed to me to be out of place, for it stands in the middle of a field, with no fence on either side, and I could not help wondering why anyone should have thought of building such a fine modern piece of architecture in such an out-of-the-way spot.

But as I drew nearer I discovered the reason, for this arch stands on the invisible line that separates Canada from the United States, a border that stretches over three thousand five hundred miles, through forests, prairies, lakes, and mountains, from one coast to the other, without a single fortification or gun emplacement of any kind. It is truly a frontier of peace.

This beautiful archway is a symbol of the abiding friendship and good will that exist between the two countries.

On one side of it appear the words "Brethren Dwelling Together in Unity."

331

On the other side are words equally beautiful:
"Children of a Common Mother."

Above, one on either side, fly the flags of the two
nations, the Union Jack and the Stars and Stripes.

But somehow I was most impressed by the gates.

Gates! you say. Gates without fences!

Yes! The funniest little gates you ever saw, so small,
so thin, and so weak that, if anyone should ever close
them, the wind would blow them over!

But just above the gates, where they are suspended
on the inside of the archway, appears this glorious
expression of hope:

"May these gates never be closed."

Wouldn't it be a lovely thing if such archways
could be planted on the frontiers of all nations? Indeed,
if such tokens of good will and friendliness could re-
place all the forts and fences, all the dugouts and
trenches, that stretch over so many thousands of miles
of the earth's surface, what a happy place the world
would be to live in! What a lot of its problems would
be suddenly solved!

Though this may be impossible with things as they
are, it should not hinder us, as boys and girls, from
building peace arches wherever we can and always
trying to look at other children and their problems
through them.

Although we cannot alter the frontiers of nations,

we can at least see to it that there are no barriers of
enmity between our hearts and other hearts anywhere
in the world. In all our relations with other people—
with the children at school, or the people next door,
rich or poor, cultured or ignorant—let us remember
that we are "children of a common Mother." So far
as lies in our power let us be "brethren dwelling
together in unity." Let the gates of our hearts be open
to all, with no national or racial boundaries to our sympathy and love.

Thus, each in our little way, we may extend the
frontiers of peace.

**Tommy Loved to Play With His Precious Trucks and Cars on the Driveway. He Would Make "Roads" for Them and Imagine They Were Real Roads and Trucks**

# Tommy's Trucks

 $\mathcal{T}$ OMMY WAS ONLY A
very little boy, but he had a will of his own. That is, he
liked to have his own way, and he didn't like to do what
he was told.

Now, Tommy had some beautiful little trucks and
autos, toy ones, of course, that Daddy had bought him
from time to time. He must have had a dozen trucks at
least, and as for the autos, well, there were blue cars
and orange cars and green cars and yellow cars. Some
were racers and some were just plain little Fords. There
was an ambulance too, and a fire truck, which was
Tommy's special delight.

Tommy loved to play with all his precious trucks
and cars on the front porch, though sometimes he
would take them out to the driveway which led to
the garage. Then he would make "roads" for them in
the soft gravel and imagine that they were all real.

Of course, Tommy was supposed to bring them
indoors every evening after he had finished playing, but
that was something he never wanted to do. He would
say that it didn't matter; that he would bring them in

later; that it would be all right to leave them out all night ready for him to play with in the morning.

One afternoon he was particularly determined that he wouldn't bring them in. "No," he said, "I'll bring them in after a while. I'm not ready yet."

"But, Tommy," urged Mother, "something may happen to them out there. They might be stolen; a car might run over them."

"They'll be all right," said Tommy. "Nothing has happened to them so far."

"But you'd be very sorry if something did," said Mother. "You know you would."

"I'll bring them in after supper."

"It'll be dark then. Bring them in now."

"Later on."

"I said now, Tommy."

"All right."

But Tommy didn't bring them in. He went to the front door and then forgot all about them.

By and by, after dark, two big headlights came flashing up the drive. It was Daddy coming home.

"Oh, mind my trucks! Mind my cars!" shouted Tommy.

Alas, it was too late.

Crunch! Crunch! Crunch!

Daddy's big car had run over them all.

The ambulance was flat as a pancake; the fire-truck engine was completely wrecked; the racing cars would never race again.

"Oh, look what you've done! Look what you've done!" cried Tommy, rushing outside, shining a flashlight over all his ruined toys and sorrowfully picking them up, one by one.

4-22

"I'm sorry," said Daddy. "I'm dreadfully sorry."

"You don't need to be," said Mother. "Tommy was told to bring them in long ago."

"Oh, my poor cars!" wailed Tommy. "Oh, my poor fire truck! Why did you run over them?"

"You should know why," said Mother. "Remember how many times I spoke to you about them?"

"I forgot," cried Tommy, "and now they're all smashed up. There isn't one whole one left. Oh, what shall I do?"

It was a doleful procession that went indoors.

"I suppose," whispered Daddy to Mother, "I'll have to go downtown again right now."

"Not yet," whispered Mother. "Let us wait and see whether he has learned his lesson."

They did not have to wait long.

Tommy had learned his lesson all right. After this experience he decided to do exactly what Mother said, *just when she said it.*

Perhaps I should add that, all in good time, Daddy and Tommy *did* go on a little trip downtown together, Tommy looking very happy and very much excited on the front seat of Daddy's car.

Can you guess what they brought back with them?

# "I'm Here, Sir!"

*M*AURICE!" CRIED
Daddy. "Here, I want you!"

There was no reply. Daddy proceeded with his work. A big load of firewood, ordered for the winter's fuel, had been dropped on the sidewalk, and he was hurrying to get it all in the woodshed before nightfall.

After a while he called again, rather more insistently.

"Maurice! Where are you?"

Still no reply.

Daddy wondered whether he should leave the pile of wood and go in search of his son or continue with the job by himself. He decided to go on working.

In a little while, however, he began thinking about Maurice. "Why shouldn't the boy come and help?" he asked himself. Probably he was indoors somewhere in a comfortable armchair, reading a book.

He called again, somewhat angrily this time.

"Maurice! I'm waiting for you."

"Ye-ah," drawled a sleepy voice from somewhere in the house. "Did you call me?"

339

"I should think I did call you," said Daddy. "Come along quickly and help carry this wood into the shed."

There was a long pause.

"Are you coming, Maurice," asked Daddy, "or shall I have to come and fetch you?"

"Aw, I suppose I'll have to come," said the sleepy voice. And in a few minutes Maurice, hands in pockets, came out the front door.

"What did you want me to do?" he asked.

"Surely you can see for yourself," said Daddy. "We must move this wood off the sidewalk before nightfall. Hurry up now."

At long last Maurice began to bestir himself and was soon busily lifting the logs into the wheelbarrow for

Daddy to wheel to the shed. He could work all right once he got going; but he badly needed a self-starter.

When the job was finished, and the last log had been carried in, Daddy turned to Maurice.

"Thanks, son," he said. "You're a great help. I like to have you working with me. If only you would come the first thing when you are called, you'd be perfect. I wonder if you could improve along that line?"

"Aw, it's always hard to get started," said Maurice, "especially when I'm interested in something else."

"Let me tell you a story," said Daddy.

Maurice was "all ears" at once. He loved stories.

"Do you remember hearing or reading of a man called Shackleton—Sir Ernest Shackleton?"

"You mean the famous explorer who went to the South Pole?"

"Yes. Well, once when he was planning an expedition to the Antarctic he decided he must take someone called Wild with him, a man who had been a most faithful and devoted helper on former trips. But Wild was nowhere to be found. It was said that he had gone big-game hunting in the heart of Africa, and there was no way to reach him.

" 'You had better give up trying to locate him,' said a friend. 'If he's in Africa, you'll never find him. What's more, if he's big-game hunting, he won't want to go to the Antarctic again anyway.'

" 'But I must have Wild along with me,' said Shackleton.

" 'Better sail without him,' said his friend. 'You can't find him, and if you could, he wouldn't go.'

" 'If Wild knows I am going on this trip, he will come,' said Shackleton. 'I'm sure he will, whether he is in Africa or anywhere else.'

" 'Not a bit of it,' said his friend.

"Just then there was a knock on the door. It was a messenger boy with a card in his hand.

" 'There's a gentleman downstairs to see you, sir,' he said. 'Shall I bring him up?'

"Shackleton looked at the card.

"He read: 'Frank Wild.'

" 'It's Wild! He's here!' he cried. 'Bring him in.'

"Beaming with smiles, the old friends met and shook hands.

" 'But how, why——?' began Shackleton. 'I thought you were hunting big game in Africa.'

" 'I was, sir,' said Wild. 'But I heard you were going on this expedition; so I dropped everything and came at once.'

"Then, standing stiffly at attention and saluting, he said, 'I'm here, sir! Captain, what are your orders?'

"Now, Maurice, don't you think that Wild did a splendid thing? He didn't wait to be called. He just felt that he was needed and came along. He dropped everything he was doing and hurried to what he felt was his post of duty."

"That was grand of him," said Maurice.

"I wish——" began Daddy.

"I know," said Maurice.

He did.

Next time Daddy called him to help on a job, a cheerful voice replied immediately:

"I'm here, sir! Captain, what are your orders?"

# The Price of Success

*F*OR YEARS AND YEARS people dreamed about throwing a bridge across the Golden Gate at San Francisco, but few men thought it could be done. There was the swift tide to battle with, and the fact that the span must be high enough above the channel to permit the largest ships in the world to pass under.

There was only one way, and that was to build a gigantic suspension bridge with a single span of over four thousand feet in length and more than two hundred feet above the water. Could it be done? Some said yes, and many said no. A few brave men determined to try.

344

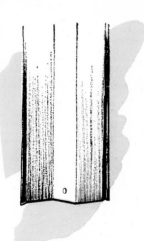

Plans were drawn, and at last the engineers began their tremendous task.

It was like stringing a clothesline down the back garden, only on a colossal scale.

First they had to erect the two gigantic posts, or towers, and these had to rest on solid concrete foundations, laid deep down on bedrock.

One of these piers had to be built far out in the water, a most difficult task. Work on this had to be conducted from barges with the tide running by sometimes at eight miles an hour, and swells from the Pacific Ocean lifting them up and down fifteen feet and more. It was no easy task, and ofttimes the workmen were seasick, but they kept right on.

To prepare the foundations, tubes were run down to the rock, and through these tubes twenty-foot bombs were lowered and exploded. Clamshell buckets with hard steel teeth brought up the broken pieces.

After this, with the barges still pitching and tossing about, steel frames were guided down to bedrock, a hundred feet below the water, followed by forms into which concrete was skillfully poured until at last a solid pier rose above the waves.

345

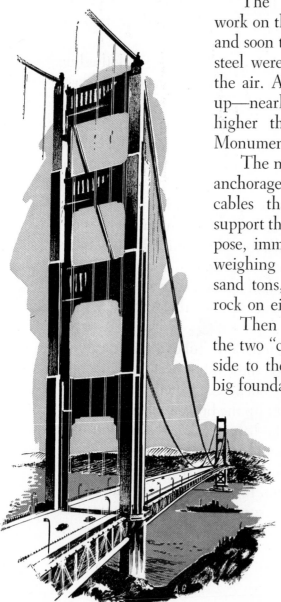

The foundations finished, work on the twin towers began, and soon these mighty pillars of steel were rising 746 feet into the air. And that's a long way up—nearly two hundred feet higher than the Washington Monument.

The next job was to provide anchorage for the great steel cables that would ultimately support the bridge. For this purpose, immense concrete blocks, weighing more than fifty thousand tons, were sunk into the rock on either side.

Then they started to carry the two "clotheslines" from one side to the other, over the two big foundation posts.

That was a fine piece of work, for they didn't try to throw the big cables across all in one piece, but strand by strand, until they had 27,572 strands hanging there for each cable, the single strands being the thickness of a lead pencil.

Then a wonderful machine was brought into action, which squeezed and squeezed and squeezed all those little strands until they became solid ropes of steel, each one three feet and half an inch in diameter. Just why they had to be half an inch over the three feet I do not know, but that is what they are.

The "clotheslines" safely fastened, the next task was to build the framework of the roadway and suspend it from the great steel ropes. Working gradually outward from both sides, they at last met in the middle, and great was the rejoicing when the last girder was laid.

Yet there was still much to be done, and it was months before the barriers were withdrawn and the tide of traffic began to roll over the Golden Gate for the first time in history.

Someday, if possible, you must see this magnificent bridge, for it is by far the largest single-span bridge in the world, and no one is ever likely to build one any bigger, unless it be over the English Channel or Bering Straits!

Everything about it is huge, whether you think of its 20,000-ton towers, or the 80,000 miles of cable wire required for the steel ropes, or the 300,000 cubic yards of concrete in the foundations, or the 110,000 gallons of paint to protect it from rust. The roadway itself is ninety feet in width, providing six lanes for traffic.

It is indeed one of the greatest wonders of the modern world.

Of course, it cost a lot of money, about thirty-two million dollars, but nothing truly great and glorious has ever been achieved without effort and expense.

And whether we think of the building of bridges, or of railways, or of ships, or of hospitals, or of Christian missions, or anything that has ever contributed to human welfare, there has always been a price to pay, and sometimes a heavy price, too.

Which reminds me of the story told about a famous Chinese emperor who commanded his chief metalsmith to make a fabulously large bell. It was to be bigger than any bell ever made, and the most beautiful in tone.

Cast after cast was made, but the metal would not set perfectly. Each cast showed a crack.

The chief metalsmith became anxious, for he feared the wrath of his master, should he fail in his task. His young and beautiful daughter sought to comfort him, and suggested he consult some of the wise men of the realm.

Taking her advice, he learned from the wise men that the molten metal would not set perfectly unless mixed with human flesh.

But how could he do that?

Once more the metalsmith lit his fires, more fearful than ever of failure as the boiling metal was poured into the mighty mold. Would it set? or would it crack again?

Suddenly, to his horror, his little daughter, leaping over the side of the mold, flung herself into the bubbling, white-hot mass.

She vanished, but the bell was perfect, with a tone never heard before on land or sea.

Heroism, endurance, sacrifice—these are the qualities that have built every worth-while thing the world has ever seen.

And if you would build something great someday with that little life of yours, you must be willing to throw yourself into it with all your heart.

"Whatsoever thy hand findeth to do," said Solomon the wise, "do it with thy might."

Halfhearted service will never get you anywhere; it takes everything there is of you to achieve success in anything.

# A Boy in Chains

THE OTHER DAY I SAW a strange sight in New York City. Yes, actually, it was a boy in chains.

"What!" you say, "a boy in chains nowadays?"

Yes, a real, live slave boy, despite the fact that Abraham Lincoln has been dead a long time.

The boy was quite small, which made me think that he was very young, but his face had a strange, oldish look, so that I couldn't tell just what his age might be. Particularly I was struck with the fact that he was puffing away at a cigarette like a grownup. So I decided to speak to him.

"How is it that you

350

are smoking at your age?" I asked him kindly.

"Can't help it, mister," he replied, with amazing frankness.

"Can't help it?" I repeated. "That's very strange. How old are you?"

"Just thirteen."

"Just thirteen!" I exclaimed. "Then how long have you been smoking?"

"Three years, mister."

"Three years!" I said, aghast. "You mean to tell me you have been smoking since you were ten?"

"Yes, mister. The other boys smoked, so I started, too."

"What other boys?"

"All the boys in my grade at school.

And most of the seventh grade smoke, too, mister."

"And the sixth?"

"Yes, mister. Even some in the sixth. I know; I've seen them."

I was horrified, wondering how many boy slaves to the smoking habit there must be in the country nowadays.

"And now you can't give it up," I said.

"That's right, mister. I can't. I've tried, but it's no good."

"Then you're a slave," I said.

"Yes, mister. That's about it. I am."

A slave at thirteen!

"You'll be terribly sorry later on," I said. "You are poisoning yourself. You will never be able to do well in play or in work if you go on like this."

"I know," he said. "Sort of gets your wind; you can't run so fast. I've felt it myself out on the school playground."

So he had noticed the terrible effect of tobacco already. At thirteen!

Poor little slave!

We talked on awhile about the harm that smoking does, and the importance of breaking the habit right away.

"You will have to summon all your will power," I said to him, "and put your foot down now."

"Maybe after I have smoked these," he said, pointing to the big packet that was bulging from his coat pocket.

"No," I said firmly. "If you want to stop it, there's only one time to do it."

"And that's now," he said with a smile. "I know."

That raised my hopes.

"You're right, son," I said. "You have the idea. Stop now, and throw the rest away. Will you?"

"I think I will," he said.

"Good boy!" I replied. "Promise me that you'll never touch the horrid things again."

"All right."

We shook hands on it, and I sent up a little prayer that Jesus would help him in the struggle which I knew he was bound to have.

Then we parted.

My little slave friend had come very near to freedom. His chains were unloosed.

Did he step out of them into a new life of liberty?

Did he keep his promise?

I wonder. I hope he did.

# Jesus Told Her

*T*HE LITTLE GIRL IN this story was only three years old when she did this lovely thing I am going to tell you about. What a great deal of good even a tiny three-year-old can do!

Her Father is an important businessman, a very important one, but not long ago he became very, very ill. He was so sick that two doctors were called in, and the servants in the great big house where he lived were told to go about their work without making the least little bit of noise, so that the master would not be disturbed.

Nobody was allowed in the sickroom except the nurse and the doctors. They were most particular about this. There was to be no troubling of the patient for any reason whatever, they said. If he did not sleep, then there would be no hope of saving his life.

And that was just what the patient could not do. Sleep would not come. Hour after hour he tossed about, restless and irritable, and constantly getting weaker.

As the days passed and he became steadily worse, the doctors finally decided that there was nothing more that they could do. It was only a matter of time, they said, and the family had better prepare for the worst.

All this time little Gloria had been consumed with curiosity regarding what was going on in the darkened room. She knew her dear Daddy was sick in there, but she couldn't understand why she was not allowed to go in, why she had to be kept so far away from him.

Now and then, when nobody was looking, she would creep along to the door of the sickroom and stand outside listening, as quiet as a little pussy hunting a mouse. There she would stay until the nurse opened the door, and then she would run away so fast that there was no time for the nurse to blame her for being there.

How little Gloria did want to see her Daddy! She felt that he needed her, and it made her so cross to be told that she mustn't go into his room any more.

Then one afternoon, as she was looking around a corner of the corridor, sadly watching the door of

Daddy's room, the nurse came out and walked down to the bathroom. And she left the door open!

Like a streak of lightning Gloria sped around the corner and into the room. She just *had* to see her Daddy, and you couldn't blame her very much, could you?

But when she saw her Daddy she felt very sad. He looked so pale and tired.

"Poor Daddy!" she said, gently touching his hand. "I'm so sorry." And then after a pause, "I love you, Daddy."

Daddy turned his head and smiled weakly at her. "I'm glad you came to see me," he whispered, trying to stroke her golden curls.

Tears filled Gloria's eyes, and all of a sudden she walked over to the window and looked up into the sky. And there she talked quietly to Jesus, just as though she were talking to a very dear friend. In a moment or two she was back again at her Daddy's bedside.

"Daddy," she said very earnestly, with her sweet little face aglow with happiness, "Jesus told me just now that you are going to get better."

Daddy smiled and slowly closed his eyes.

Just then Gloria heard footsteps. It was the nurse coming back! But Gloria didn't even think of running to hide. It was her turn now.

"Ssssh!" she said, as the nurse came in, an angry

frown on her face. "Ssssh! my Daddy's asleep. Don't wake him up."

The nurse looked, and to her amazement she saw that Gloria was right. Her patient was asleep at last. The little girl had done more than all the doctors and the nurses together.

The poor sick man, whom everybody had given up to die, slept soundly all that night, something he had not done for many weeks. In the morning, when he awoke, he was so much better that the doctors could hardly believe their eyes. And he kept on getting better until soon he was his old self again.

Today he is back at his work, but he never tires of telling the story of how his life was saved, not by the doctors, but by his own little Gloria and the prayer she prayed at the window that afternoon.

# Holding On

$S$OME TIME AGO, WHEN
visiting a large garage where busses are repaired, I
noticed something which interested me very much.

Everything was on the move.

The movement was so slow that at first I did not
notice it; but as I watched carefully, I began to realize
that from the moment the damaged bus came in to be
overhauled, it never stopped until it went out of the
garage again.

That sounds funny, I know, but it is a fact; the
reason being that underneath the floor there is an end-
less steel wire gently moving along all the time. To this
each bus is attached as soon as it enters the building,
and everything that is done to it happens as it passes on
its way. Cleaners, painters, upholsterers, mechanics,
are waiting all along the line to do their part, until at
last the bus goes out on the road once more so spick and
span you would think it was brand new.

Let's watch one of the old busses coming in, and see
what happens to it. What a sight it is, with its mudguards all dented, its paint work scratched, its windows

cracked. This one has evidently been in a smashup.

First of all, as it passes under a powerful crane, giant arms embrace the body and lift it off the chassis, which is driven off to its own section for attention.

The body, on a trolley, is attached to the evermoving wire, and starts off on its two-day trip through the big garage.

Men appear on the scene and remove the dented mudguards and the bent steel plates, and hurry them away to the foundry to get them straightened out. Other men enter the bus and start to remove the seats for recovering. Painters stand by, ready to apply the first coat of fresh paint.

Meanwhile the chassis, also gripping the evermov-

ing wire in its own section, is being quickly torn apart, every bolt and nut being removed, tested, and renewed where necessary. Engine, brakes, wheels, all are detached, taken to pieces, and passed through a mighty washing machine to remove all grease and dirt. Then, as the frame moves on and on, its parts, polished all shiny bright, are returned to it.

Wheels, brakes, engine, and the rest are all replaced, and just as it begins to look the way a chassis ought to look, it sees its old body just ahead, resplendent in its coat of new paint, all ready waiting for it.

The two are reunited, and not long afterward the garage doors open, and the bus, now renovated from end to end, rolls out onto the road once more.

Just think a minute. How and why did this marvelous change take place?

Because the dilapidated old thing held on to the moving wire! If the bus had said to itself, "I don't want to have my old plates, my old seats, and my old mudguards removed; I don't want to have my worn-out engine taken to pieces; I don't want to put up with all this trouble; I'm not going to hold on to this wire"— well, then it would have remained just a dilapidated old bus, wouldn't it?

But it held on to the wire, and was changed.

And it's just that way with all of us, children. The dear Lord Jesus wants to take every life that has been spoiled by sin, and make it over again. He wants to clean up, not only the outside paint work, but every nut and bolt and screw and washer in our engines, with brakes and wheels and all the rest.

He has His own way of doing it too, and it never fails, if He is given full sway.

So if you want to be made over again, and have all the bumps and dents and scratches taken away from your character, just tell Him all about it, take hold of His love, and He will lead you through the very experiences you need to make you all He wants you to be.

Some things may happen that you may not like. But do not worry or become discouraged. Tell yourself it is just the dents being knocked out.

Some experiences may seem rather hard and discouraging, but never mind; these represent the scratches being sandpapered.

If you know you are *holding on to Jesus,* you may be sure that all will be well in the end. You may come to Him in the worst possible mess, but if you will yield yourself into His hands He will make such a wonderful change in you that you won't know yourself.

In place of selfishness He will give you a spirit of willing sacrifice. Anger and impatience will be replaced by sweet gentleness. Quarrelsomeness will give way to happy friendliness.

Indeed, there's no end to what may happen if you will just take hold of that golden cord of everlasting love that links earth to heaven and moves onward and upward into the kingdom of God.

It's just a matter of holding on.

# Happy, Happy Land

*I*T WAS ONE OF THOSE sultry, suffocating summer days in Washington, D.C.

Everybody was hot and tired and sticky.

Whether you walked or whether you stood still, you were bathed in perspiration.

A clean shirt lasted twenty minutes, a collar, five.

The city appeared deserted, for the heat had driven nearly all the people off the streets. But it was almost as hot inside as out, and just as stifling.

At noon I went into a restaurant. The customers all looked about as depressed as I felt. It was too hot to eat; too hot to care about anything or anybody.

Just then I noticed a young girl waiting on the people, her face aglow with smiles. The contrast was so striking that I watched her awhile.

She would come to tables at which people were sitting, tired, hot, and irritable, and smile at them so cheerfully, so sincerely, that she made them smile back at her. And it didn't make any difference who it was. She had the same happy greeting for everybody. The whole big restaurant was cheered by her presence.

At suppertime that same day I thought I would go back to the same place to eat, just to see if that unusually happy little soul had lost her radiance.

The evening was hotter than the day. It was almost too much trouble to drag my weary legs to the restaurant. But there, sure enough, smiling still, was the same cheerful waitress. I confess I felt a bit ashamed of myself, for I had rested while she had worked, and lo, here I was still tired, while she was working away, as bright and cheerful as ever.

The hotter the day, the cooler she seemed. The

more others frowned, the more she smiled. As others became harder to please, she became more willing to help them.

Then an idea came to me. Suppose everybody should have a sweet spirit like that, and a smile like that, what a happy place this old world would be to live in!

Haven't you noticed how pleasant it is to talk to people who smile at you? It cheers you up, doesn't it? Makes you feel good. Makes you want to smile at them.

While I was sitting there in that restaurant looking on, unnoticed, at the inspiring little scene, my mind went back to a hymn I used to sing in church long ago:

"There is a happy land,
Far, far away."

Maybe you have sung it, too.

Then I began to wonder what it will be that will make that land so happy.

It's going to have golden streets, so we're told, and

pearly gates and jasper walls. There'll be a sea of "glass mingled with fire," and a beautiful river with many, many glorious trees and flowers growing all about it. And there'll be magnificent mansions for us all to live in. And there'll be marvelous lighting arrangements, and air conditioning, so that it will never be too hot or too cold. But will it be all these wonderful attractions and conveniences that will make the people happy, and keep them happy?

No. I don't think so.

There are many people about nowadays with beautiful homes and gardens who are the grumpiest people on earth, and the hardest to get along with. And there are many children with heaps and heaps of toys and other good things, who are perfect little demons. Maybe you know some of them.

No, it isn't the possession of beautiful things that will make heaven a happy place in which to live. Rather, it will be the joy in the people's hearts, and the smiles on their faces.

There won't be a single disagreeable person there.

Not one. Nor anybody with a grouch or a grumble, or any hard feelings of any sort.

And when you walk down the streets of the New Jerusalem one day—as I hope you will—you will not even notice the streets of gold or the gates of pearl for looking at the smiling faces of the people you will pass on the way.

You will be just thrilled through and through to see everybody so cheerful—especially after seeing so many people miserable and cross and grumpy down here.

From behind you and before you will come the sound of holy, happy laughter; for their mouths shall be "filled with laughter," the Bible says. Everybody will be bubbling over with joy.

And so will heaven's happiness continue forever and ever.

Won't that be wonderful?

"They shall hunger no more, neither thirst any more; neither shall the sun light on them, nor any heat. For the Lamb which is in the midst of the throne shall feed them, and shall lead them unto living fountains of

waters: and God shall wipe away all tears from their eyes." Revelation 7:16, 17.

"And the ransomed of the Lord shall return, and come to Zion with songs and everlasting joy upon their heads: they shall obtain joy and gladness, and sorrow and sighing shall flee away." Isaiah 35:10.

That will be a heaven worth waiting for, worth hoping for, worth living for.

Wouldn't you like to be there?

Well, you may be, if you wish. But first you must let Jesus take out of your heart everything that would spoil that lovely place. Every mean thought must go, with every unkind motive, everything that is cruel, coarse, rude, unfriendly, or impolite. For nothing that might harm anybody else or ruin anyone's happiness may enter there.

Jesus can do this for you. He can change you and make you fit to live in His beautiful heaven. That is why He came to this world—to cleanse us from every evil thing and make us ready to enjoy the wonderful new world of eternal joy and blessedness which He is preparing for His children.

Strangely enough, while we are preparing for the happiness of the next world, we shall be happier in this!

And the frowns will vanish, the grumbles will cease, the hard words will disappear. In their place the smiles will come, and a cheerfulness that will lighten the darkness around us like radiance from heaven itself.

That's how you may get to the happy, happy land, "far, far away."

Let's start on the road to it now.

HARRY ANDERSON, ARTIST

"I Will Come Again." What a Glorious and Joyful Morning That Will Be When
We Shall See Him Coming in the Clouds of Heaven

# Is This the Morning?

*H*OW THAT BOY OF mine does love the sea! You should just see him some time holding the wheel of one of those motorboats they have at some seaside resorts; and is he happy!

When I took him in a big speedboat the other day, and left him all alone on the back seat, the look of perfect bliss on his face was something wonderful to behold.

Then, some years ago, as we were driving through British Columbia, I happened to let the word fall that we might be going on a big steamer soon.

Alas, for our peace!

"When are we going on the big steamer, Daddy?" he asked. "How many funnels does it have? Will it have lots of smoke? Will it go very fast? Shall we go far, far away? Will it be the *Queen Mary?*"

But the chief question was always, "When are we going, Daddy? Will it be tomorrow?"

"No," I said, "not tomorrow."

"Then how soon?"

"Very, very soon."

"Oh, dear, I can hardly wait!"

So the days went by, with the same questions being asked over and over again, the inquiry always being finished with that plaintive plea, "Will it be very soon now?"

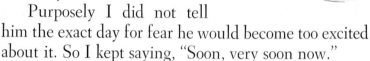

Purposely I did not tell him the exact day for fear he would become too excited about it. So I kept saying, "Soon, very soon now."

Then one day we crossed the Canadian border, drove on down to the port of Seattle, and stayed there for the night, so as to be in good time to catch the boat in the morning.

But we did not tell the boy. Oh, dear, no. He wouldn't have slept a wink. Neither would we.

So when he asked again, as he went to sleep, "Are we going on the boat soon, Daddy?" I said, "Oh, yes, *very*, very soon now," at which his weary little head fell on the pillow as though he were quite content. Little did he realize that he was so near to the goal of his dreams.

Now whether or not it was because he had slept within a quarter mile of that ship I cannot say, but he awoke early the next day with the certain conviction in his heart that the great moment had arrived.

Rubbing his little eyes and looking up earnestly into his Mother's face, he said with an eagerness I shall never forget, *"Is this the morning?"*

"Oh, yes," I said, responding to the light of hope and joy blazing in his eyes. "Yes, this is the morning. This is the day you have been waiting for so long. Today we shall go on the big steamer and see the masts and the funnels and all the smoke and things, and ride over the great big waves."

Is this the morning?

Ever since then the words have rung in my ears like a chime of lovely bells.

I have thought of all the people who have been waiting such a long, long time for the glorious morning of eternity, and how happy they will be when it breaks.

There are some people alive today who have been waiting nearly a hundred years for Jesus to come. They have not known the time of His coming, but, oh, how they have longed for it! And they have comforted their old hearts by saying, It must be soon now; there's not much longer to wait!

What joy will be theirs "in the morning"!

I have thought, too, of all the people who have endured sickness and pain, blindness and deafness, and all sorts of dreadful injuries—and how glad they will be "in the morning" when Jesus comes back to open the eyes of the blind, to unstop the ears of the deaf, and to make the lame man leap as a hart! How wonderful it will be to witness their joy as they are suddenly healed by His wondrous power, never to be sick again!

I have thought also of all those who have experienced great hardship and poverty, who have lived in slums and tenements, rarely seeing trees or flowers, or the beauty of the country or the sea—and what ecstasy of delight will be theirs "in the morning" when they discover that they will never be poor again, that Jesus has come to bring them riches enough to last forever and ever, and food enough so they will never know the pangs of hunger again; oh, yes, and when they find that He has planned for them a new heaven and a new earth more lovely than they ever imagined in their brightest dreams!

I have thought, too, of all the exiles, the people who have been driven away from their homes and countries by cruel, persecuting tyrants, and how they must have cried as they wandered homeless over the earth, and how thrilled they will be "in the morning" to find that Jesus has made ready for them the very mansions that long ago He promised to prepare for His children, a home eternal that shall never be taken away.

I have thought, also, of all the children of God who have gone to sleep in death through all the ages since sin first entered this old world, and how marvelous it

will be for them when Jesus comes to wake them from their long, long slumber.

Hundreds and thousands of them were loving Fathers and Mothers who passed away, longing for their children, and countless others were children who died, longing to see their parents once again; and one day soon upon their waiting ears will fall the beautiful voice of Jesus calling them forth from the grave.

Can you not hear them all crying in glad, incredulous surprise, "Jesus, *is this the morning?*"

What a glad reunion there will be that day!

Many will be the martyrs of Jesus—men, women, and children, too, who chose to be tortured and killed rather than give up their faith in Him. Lots and lots of them perished miserably in dungeons, waiting so patiently for the deliverance that never came.

Can you not hear them crying, almost frantic with joy, as the Master for whom they gave up so much bends over them in tender love and calls them from the tomb to spend eternity with Him, "O Jesus, is this the morning for which we have waited so long?"

Some people talk about the coming of Jesus as a day of darkness, gloom, and misery, but for all who love Him it is going to be the happiest day in history. That's why the apostle Paul calls it "the blessed hope." It's going to be the most wonderful, the most glorious, and the most joyous event that ever happened.

Every one of us should be looking forward to it with the keenest joy, just as Jesus Himself must be longing, too, for the great day to dawn.

In my front garden, down by the gate, there is the trunk of a dead pepper tree that we cut down some time ago. The top is flat and makes a dear little seat, and there is a step so that one can climb up onto it.

For years this was my youngest boy's seat, where he would sit and wait for his Daddy to come home.

It used to make going home so thrilling to think he would be there. When I was still a long way off he would see me and there would be a mighty yelling and a great waving of hands.

And it seems to me that this is how Jesus would have us await His coming—sitting high up on the pepper tree, as it were, looking eagerly down the road, "waiting and watching for Him."

And I believe that just as I would take up my little boy and hug him because he was waiting there at the gate for me, so Jesus will gather us into His everlasting arms of love and tell us He is glad we did the same for Him.

Then we will all go in together to partake of "the marriage supper of the Lamb," and to hear Him say to everybody, "Come, ye blessed of My Father, inherit the kingdom prepared for you from the foundation of the world." And it will all be so wonderful, so unbelievably beautiful, that we shall cry out in rapture once more—

"Is this the morning?"

# The Hall of Portraits

BRUCE WAS THE ELD-
est son of a Scottish lord, and heir to all his Father's
great estate.

Now he was leaving home to go to boarding school,
and he and his Father were having a final chat before
they said good-by.

"Let us walk down the hall," said Father; "there is
something I want to show you there."

Bruce had walked down that grand old hall many
a time, thinking of it only as a passageway between the
front entrance and the majestic ballroom at the other
end of the castle, but suddenly it became something
quite different.

"Look up at the walls," said Father, and Bruce,
looking, saw the familiar portraits he had seen since he
was a little child. They lined the walls on either side
and were the work of many a famous artist.

"These men," said Father, "are your ancestors. It
is the record of them all that they never once did a dishonorable deed. If they could speak, they would tell
you they expect you to follow their example. One day,

if time should last, your portrait will also adorn these walls, and it must be without disgrace. The tradition of the family must not be broken."

That was all, but Bruce never forgot. At school, at college, and in afterlife the memory of that hall of portraits remained, keeping him from all pettiness and folly and ever inspiring him to great and noble deeds.

What a fine thing it would be if all of us could carry a similar glowing memory all through life!

Of course, there are not many of us who live in castles and the pictures of our humble ancestors are most probably hidden away in some photograph album, or moldering in some old box in the attic. Our homes aren't big enough nowadays to have a hall of portraits, anyway; and if they were, we probably would want to hang some different kind of picture.

Yet all of us, if we will, may build up in our minds a hall of portraits of our own, hanging there the pictures of all the great and noble men we have ever known or read about, the memory of whom will help to keep us loyal and true to what we know to be right.

David Livingstone

Whom would you put there? Perhaps the portrait of a lovely Mother, a self-sacrificing Father, some gallant missionary, some martyred Reformer, some fearless hero of a great crusade.

Perhaps I could make some suggestions.

Personally, I would want to start with a few of the great Bible characters. From the Old Testament I think I would choose Moses, who freed Israel from the bondage of Egypt, and Elijah, the prophet who so gallantly championed God's cause in a time of great wickedness. Then from the New Testament I would choose the apostle Paul because of his wonderful faith and courage, and the apostle John because of his devoted love for his Master.

On another part of my hall of portraits I would display the pictures of the great Reformers, beginning with John Wycliffe, known as the Morning Star of the Reformation. Beside him I would like to see John Huss of Bohemia, Martin Luther of Germany, and William Tyndale, who gave us our English Bible.

Farther on would begin my portraits of missionaries, and there I would have William Carey, the cobbler who went to India, Hudson Taylor of China, and David Livingstone and Robert Moffat, who opened up Africa to the gospel. With them, too, I would place more modern missionaries, such as F. A. Stahl, who carried the gospel to the Indians of the Amazon, and Captain Jones, who braved the cannibals of the South Sea Islands for Christ's sake.

Beside these I would hang the portraits of the great humanitarians, like George Müller, who did so

much for the orphans; old William Booth, who spent his life for the poor; Florence Nightingale, the mother of modern nursing; and Andrew Carnegie, whose free libraries are a memorial to his name.

Oh, yes, and I would want to have the portraits of some of the great explorers, too—brave men like Columbus, the discoverer of America, Sir Ernest Shackleton and Ad-

**Florence Nightingale**

miral Byrd, of South Pole fame, and Commander Peary, who found the North Pole.

I would gladly display as well some of the noble statesmen who have guided their countries through great crises, men like Gladstone, prime minister of England, and our great Washington and Lincoln.

**Abraham Lincoln**

**While James Watt Sat in His Home Watching the Kettle Boil He Was Thinking. He Discovered the Power of Steam That Drives Our Great Engines and Big Ships Today**

I would also want to have some of the pioneers of discovery in science and medicine, such as Thomas Edison, who gave us electric lights; James Watt, who invented the steam engine; Madame Curie who discovered radium; and Marconi, who invented wireless.

And I wouldn't be forgiven if I didn't want also the pictures of men who have done much for modern engineering—Henry Ford in the auto industry, Steinmetz, the wizard of electrical energy, and Einstein, the father of atomic physics.

But what about great poets like Milton, who wrote *Paradise Lost;* and Tennyson, who wrote that delightful poem every boy loves, *The Charge of the Light Brigade;* or Longfellow, who penned those stirring lines, *The Building of the Ship.* He wrote also *The Village Blacksmith,* and so many others we loved to read in school.

There are those of you who would feel bad if we didn't have some great artists represented too, such as Michelangelo, Raphael, and Rembrandt. And musicians, what a lot of them deserve to have a place in our hall of great men! We could only make a start with Johann Bach, Chopin, Beethoven, and Handel who wrote that wonderful "Hallelujah Chorus" in his *Messiah.*

Oh, dear! What a lot of pictures! My hall doesn't seem nearly big enough to hang them all. I am going to

suggest, however, that you reserve one wall all by itself
for the greatest portrait of all. For Jesus, who inspired
so many of these great men and women to great deeds,
deserves the most beautiful picture any artist could
paint, and the most prominent place in our Hall of
Portraits. And if you make His life the standard by
which you judge the worthiness of all the other great
men you would honor, you will never hang a picture
of anyone who ever did a dishonorable deed. Then
their fragrant and stimulating memory will inspire you,
as they inspired Bruce, to follow in their steps, and give
your life to some of the noble and heroic tasks still waiting to be done.

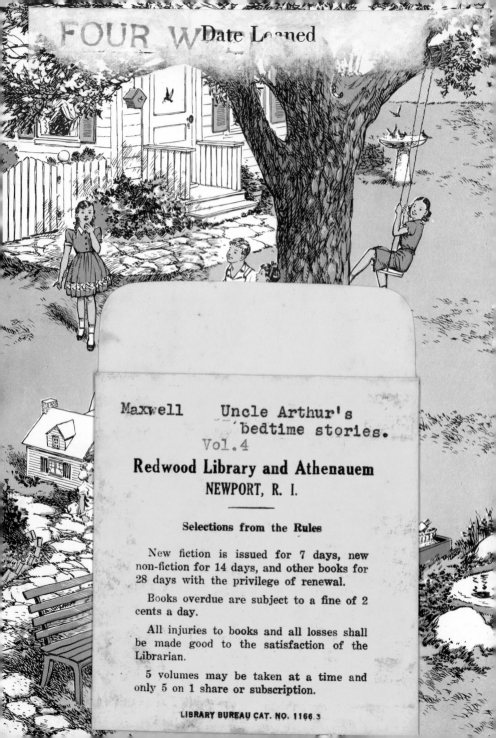